29/04/22

D0914114

Asa Johal
and Terminal Forest Products

Asa Johal
and Terminal
Forest Products

How a Sikh Immigrant Created BC's Largest
Independent Lumber Company

———————

JINDER OUJLA-CHALMERS

———————

Harbour Publishing Co. Ltd.
P.O. Box 219, Madeira Park, BC, VON 2HO
www.harbourpublishing.com

Unless otherwise noted, all photos are from the Asa Johal Family Collection.
Edited by Betty Keller
Indexed by Michelle Chiang
Dust jacket design by Anna Comfort O'Keeffe and Michelle Chiang
Text design by Shed Simas / Onça Design
Printed and bound in Canada
Printed on paper certified by the Forest Stewardship Council

Harbour Publishing acknowledges the support of the Canada Council for the Arts, which last year invested $153 million to bring the arts to Canadians throughout the country.

Nous remercions le Conseil des arts du Canada de son soutien. L'an dernier, le Conseil a investi 153 millions de dollars pour mettre de l'art dans la vie des Canadiennes et des Canadiens de tout le pays.

We also gratefully acknowledge financial support from the Government of Canada and from the Province of British Columbia through the BC Arts Council and the Book Publishing Tax Credit.

Library and Archives Canada Cataloguing in Publication

Title: Asa Johal and Terminal Forest Products : how a Sikh immigrant created BC's largest
        independent lumber company / Jinder Oujla-Chalmers.
Names: Oujla-Chalmers, Jinder, author.
Description: Includes bibliographical references and index.
Identifiers: Canadiana (print) 20190137819 | Canadiana (ebook) 20190137835 | ISBN 9781550178890
        (hardcover) | ISBN 9781550178906 (HTML)
Subjects: LCSH: Johal, Asa | LCSH: Terminal Forest Products-History | LCSH: Businessmen-
        British Columbia-Biography. | CSH: Sikh Canadians-British Columbia-Biography |
        LCSH: Forest products industry-British Columbia-History. | LCGFT: Biographies.
Classification: LCC HD9764.C32 O95 2019 | DDC 338.1/7498092-dc23

To my mother, Jeet Kaur Oujla, who has inspired me throughout my life with her unconditional love and strength. And to Roop Johal, whose bright light continues to shine through the entire Johal family and the universe.

Table of Contents

Asa Johal's Family Tree

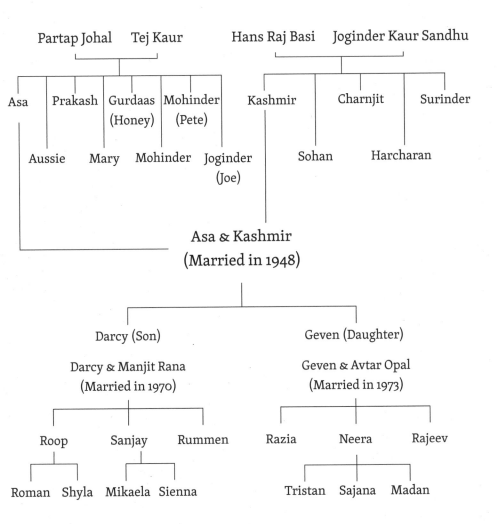

Partap Johal   Tej Kaur   Hans Raj Basi   Joginder Kaur Sandhu

Asa   Prakash   Gurdaas (Honey)   Mohinder (Pete)   Kashmir   Charnjit   Surinder

Aussie   Mary   Mohinder   Joginder (Joe)   Sohan   Harcharan

Asa & Kashmir
(Married in 1948)

Darcy (Son)   Geven (Daughter)

Darcy & Manjit Rana   Geven & Avtar Opal
(Married in 1970)   (Married in 1973)

Roop   Sanjay   Rummen   Razia   Neera   Rajeev

Roman   Shyla   Mikaela   Sienna   Tristan   Sajana   Madan

Introduction

For more than 150 years, the forest industry has traditionally been a cornerstone of BC's economy, generating tens of thousands of jobs directly and supporting many more jobs in other sectors. It was in this industry that immigrant Sikhs found jobs at the beginning of the last century as labourers in the woods and in sawmills, and even though they faced racial discrimination, they gradually broadened their range and found their place as firewood suppliers and operators of small sawmills.

When the Sikh immigrant Asa Singh Johal founded Terminal Forest Products in 1965, he was determined to build a thriving sawmill business. It was a difficult journey—getting a timber supply and establishing markets; constantly upgrading equipment to become more efficient; navigating complicated political situations, economic recessions, labour disputes and all the permutations of the softwood lumber dispute; as well as dealing with the large egos associated with the leadership of the forest industry. However, through hard work and never-ending perseverance, he established himself as a force to be reckoned with among the predominately white-owned and white-run forestry giants of British Columbia.

His entrepreneurial ability ultimately resulted in the creation of the largest privately owned and operated lumber manufacturing facility on Canada's West Coast. It allowed him to create hundreds of well-paid jobs and in time, afforded him the opportunity to become a very generous, albeit very private philanthropist in the fields of health and education. From BC to India, his numerous contributions have included gifts to the BC Children's Hospital, the Canadian Cancer Society, the Nargis Dutt Foundation, the University of British Columbia, Simon Fraser University, Quest University and the Asa Johal Auditorium in India. He is the recipient of both the Order of British Columbia and the Order of Canada.

When I was offered the opportunity to write his story, I thought it would be relatively easy to tell the down-to-earth tale of this prominent British Columbian and his family—a family that I thought I knew intimately—and the forest industry in which they have been involved for close to a century. But I soon discovered that I knew very little about them or the industry. As a result, I spent nearly two years reading newspaper articles and books and talking to mill owners, educators, government researchers and librarians. I interviewed forest industry professionals, especially my brother,

Avtar Opal, who spent hours explaining the inner workings of the sawmill business in order to provide me with an in-depth knowledge of the complex forestry world. I interviewed family members, sometimes together, sometimes singly, and along the way I was gradually able to unlock the surprising inside story of one of British Columbia's economic and socially conscious leaders, Asa Johal.

This book takes you inside one man's against-all-odds journey to multi-faceted success.

CHAPTER ONE

Partap Singh Johal

The story of Terminal Forest Products, a sizeable independently owned and operated lumber manufacturing facility on Canada's West Coast, begins in 1905 when twenty-six-year-old Partap Singh Johal left the village of Jandiala in the province of Punjab in northwestern India. His destination was Canada, which, like India, was then a part of the British Empire.

While Canada had begun as a British colony and graduated with relative ease to dominion status in 1867, India's absorption into the Empire had come about through a mixture of commerce and conquest. The British had first come as traders to India in the late fifteenth century and, in 1600, Queen Elizabeth I had granted an exclusive trading charter on the Indian subcontinent to a commercial enterprise known as the East India Company. Over the next 200 years, as its commercial interests grew to include territorial ambitions, the company established an army and set about gradually subduing India through warfare and by making alliances with various Mughal rulers. The last major area to be conquered was the powerful Sikh kingdom in the central Punjab region, which only submitted to the East India Company's rule in 1849 after the defeat of the Punjabi army at the Battle of Gujarat.

By that time the culture of the central Punjab region was already intricately interwoven with Sikhism, the religion founded in the late fifteenth century by Guru Nanak, the first of the ten gurus or "enlightened teachers" who established the tenets of this monotheistic faith. Among those tenets are daily meditation; honesty in thoughts, words and actions; and sharing with the needy whenever possible. The sixth guru, Guru Hargobind, added the Sikh duty to oppose injustice. The tenth and last guru, Gobind Singh (1666–1708), organized the Sikhs into a Khalsa, or militant brotherhood, in order to combat the continuing Moghul persecution, and he thereby merged Sikh religious, social and military duties into a single discipline. He also initiated the Five Ks of the Khalsa, which includes the rule that Sikhs do not cut their hair; a Sikh man covers his hair with a turban while a woman covers hers with a scarf. All male Sikhs take "Singh," which means *lion*, as their second name; women take "Kaur," which means *princess*, as theirs.

Nine years after the East India Company overran the kingdom of Punjab, the British government abolished the company and instituted the direct rule of India through a secretary of state for Indian Affairs and a governor general/viceroy. The new government created an elite civil service and regularized the British Indian Army, recruiting heavily in the Punjab Sikh region where the men were by then renowned as disciplined warriors; many Punjabi men also signed on to serve as police and watchmen in such outposts of the British Empire as Hong Kong, Singapore and Shanghai. In addition, the new British administration made the rich agricultural lands of Punjab province one of its prime areas for the commercialization of agriculture, sponsoring irrigation projects and building roads and railways there. As a result, land prices rose and families that wanted to profit from the new emphasis on agriculture took on debt to purchase acreage; for many families, their means of repaying this debt was to send their sons overseas to work and remit their wages home. British Columbia was a popular short-term immigration destination for these young men because it was part of the empire and because labourers were needed in BC's burgeoning logging and lumbering industries, and wages—even for unskilled workers—were rumoured to be as much as a dollar fifty to two dollars a day, a fortune compared to wages at home.

The first Sikhs to see British Columbia were the Punjabi soldiers of Britain's Hong Kong regiments who travelled through Vancouver on their way to and from London in June 1897 for the celebration of Queen Victoria's diamond jubilee. They returned to Punjab province with stories of this rich land, its dense forests, its favourable climate and its job opportunities. Over the next half-dozen years, a few more

Punjabis ventured to BC, mostly men who had served in the British Indian Army or in the Hong Kong police force, but no statistics were kept for this small vanguard; most of them seem to have returned to India within a few years, but they encouraged a growing number of their countrymen to follow in their footsteps.

The journey to Canada was long and difficult. The first leg took them two and a half days by train from Punjab in northwestern India to Calcutta in the northeast, where they waited as much as three or four weeks to book passage to Hong Kong on a freighter that would make stops along the way in Penang, Singapore and Manila to load and unload cargo. (There were no passenger ships plying this route at that time.) In Hong Kong, all Punjabi travellers underwent medical exams and then, after more weeks of waiting, were issued the health certificates they required to board a Vancouver-bound passenger liner, most likely one of the ships of the Canadian Pacific Steamship line. CPS, a subsidiary of the Canadian Pacific Railway, had inaugurated steamer service between Vancouver and Hong Kong with its first three "Empress" ships in 1891, but Canada's Chinese Immigration Act of 1885, which levied a $50 head tax on all Chinese persons entering Canada, had destroyed much of the company's intended passenger market in Asia. (The tax was increased in 1900 to $100 and a year later to $500.) To compensate for the lost market, the company advertised its fares and schedules on posters throughout India, concentrating especially in areas such as Punjab province,

in order to get the attention of possible short-term emi-
grants. By 1905 the company's ships were making regular
voyages from Hong Kong to Vancouver, including stops in
Yokohama and Victoria, in just over three weeks and charging approximately $65 (Canadian) for third-class fare.

Partap Singh Johal, the eldest child and only son of his
Punjabi parents, was one of 387 men from India—almost all
of them from Punjab province—to enter British Columbia
through the ports of Vancouver and Victoria in 1905. Another
2,124 arrived the following year and 2,623 in the year after that.
Although Partap was unmarried, most of the others had left
wives and children behind in India; only nine women immigrated between 1904 and 1920.[1] While the first newcomers
from India had been a curiosity—Vancouver's newspapers
reported excitedly on the arrival of five bearded, turbaned
Sikhs on the *Empress of India* in March 1904 and another ten
in May of that year on the *Empress of Japan*—as more and
more of them arrived, hostility developed. It was not only
that Vancouverites looked down on anyone who was neither
British nor northern European, but there was also a fear that,
as British subjects, these particular newcomers had the right
to vote in provincial and federal elections, thereby posing a
threat to the government in power. But even more importantly, there was the fear in the general populace that these
men from India—like the Chinese who had come before
them—would take their jobs.

There were, in fact, plenty of jobs to go around in BC
in the early years of the twentieth century, especially for

unskilled workers. Although the Canadian Pacific Railway was now complete from coast to coast, the company was still hiring gangs of pick-and-shovel workers to clear land to extend the line, build branch lines and sidings. The completed railway had also made it possible to sell British Columbia's lumber in eastern Canada and even in Europe, and as a result, West Coast logging and sawmilling companies were thriving. Fortunately for the newcomers, neither the railway nor the milling and logging company owners cared what colour their employees were or if they wore turbans; they were only interested in getting a workforce. They found the Punjabi Sikhs hard-working, reliable and willing to take on the most laborious and least attractive jobs. Even more importantly, they were available for lower wages than white workers.

By these turn-of-the century years, most of the larger logging outfits on the BC coast had graduated to donkey engines and railroads to harvest the gigantic Douglas firs and cedars of the rainforest. But some of the smaller companies were still taking only the accessible timber along the shoreline where trees could be dropped straight into the water or hauled to the shore by teams of horses or oxen, then towed in booms to the sawmills on Burrard Inlet. It was apparently in a camp like this on the outskirts of Vancouver that Partap Johal found his first job. The working conditions were brutal, but the company of his fellow Sikhs on the job provided him with the social and emotional support he needed and prevented him from feeling totally isolated.

But finding a job was easier than finding accommodation in Vancouver, as housing conditions were deplorable at this time. The city, which had a population of just 26,000 in 1901, had seen a massive surge in numbers, more than doubling in population by the time Partap Johal arrived in 1905, while construction of accommodations had lagged far behind the influx. He camped out for a week before having the good luck to find a rooming house in East Vancouver run by a white woman who was willing to take in Asians, but many newly arrived Sikhs lived for weeks in temporary shelters on the streets or tents in parks or in the woods outside the city limits. As Vancouver's winter climate was both wetter and colder than northern India, they suffered greatly. Alexander Monroe, a federal immigration officer, recalled that it was "a daily sight to see [the Sikhs] wandering here, there and everywhere ... half-starved, half-naked, staying in horrid and wretched hovels. The Sikhs were ordered here, excluded there, despised everywhere." They also had difficulty finding their customary food, and Monroe reported that "Indians who had money cannot always buy what they needed; some begged for food while others lived entirely on potatoes ... They all have money in their pockets to pay for whatever they want, but the trouble is they can't get it because the citizens of BC accuse them of being poorly dressed and of being dirty and having standards of living that were not comparable to the whites."

The constant discrimination meant that many Sikh workers in West Coast industries were laid off as soon as more white workers became available, and when these Sikhs were unable to find fresh employment, many of them drifted south to work on farms in Washington, Oregon and especially California. Others returned to India, but when Partap Johal lost his logging job at the coast, he followed friends to the Interior, ending up in the town of Fernie in the Elk Valley in the southeastern corner of the province.

In 1898, when the Canadian Pacific Railway had been pushing the Crowsnest Pass rail line through the Rockies so that the rich coal seams of the Elk Valley could be exploited, the company had also constructed a 60-foot by 310-foot (18 × 94-metre) sawmill at Fernie to turn out lumber for railway ties, bridges, snowsheds, station houses and water towers. The CPR sawmill and the valley's mixed forests of cedar, larch, fir, white pine, spruce and hemlock attracted the attention of American lumber concerns. Having clear-cut all the pine forests of Michigan, Wisconsin and Minnesota, they had been looking north for more timber and now homed in on the Elk Valley because it was close to prairie lumber markets on both sides of the border. The first of the Americans to arrive was the Elk Lumber and Manufacturing Company, which was controlled by two financiers from St. Paul, Minnesota, and in 1904 they constructed a $75,000 sawmill in Fernie; within three years it was turning out 25 million board feet of lumber per year. By that time, mills had also appeared at nearby Baynes Lake, Waldo, Elko, Minister, Hanbury and Flagstone, all of them built with American money and none of them milling less than 25,000 board feet a day. (Baynes Lake was the largest, milling 75,000 feet per day.)

This is where Partap's friends had been hired, and he also found work there as a sawmill hand because, although he was tall and thin, he was very strong. His son Asa recalls, "My father always did hard work. He was as strong as a bull. He could do the work of two men." However, there was no chance for any of the Punjabis or the Chinese they worked beside to rise above the menial labour of stacking, piling and shifting lumber in these mills, as all the skilled and supervisory positions were given to white, English-speaking workers. As well as having had no formal education in India—partly because everything one needed to know about farming could be learned on the land and partly because there were very few schools in the villages—the Punjabi men were hampered by knowing very little English. And they had few opportunities to learn it because they had little contact with other social groups; they not only worked together all day but also lived together, pooling their resources to minimize costs. Theirs was an all-male, non-English-speaking society, completely isolated from the larger community around them, which further contributed to that community undervaluing them.

In 1907 the government of British Columbia made the Punjabis' role as outsiders official by passing a bill to disenfranchise all natives of India not born of Anglo-Saxon parents. While this legislation had little immediate effect on Partap and his friends, as few of them were interested in voting, it began to have an effect five years later when the

Partap was initially employed at the Elk Lumber and Manufacturing
Company's mill in West Fernie, pictured here before it burned down in
1908. *Image A-08896 courtesy of the Royal BC Museum and Archives*

---

provincial government introduced a new Forest Act limiting
cutting rights on BC's forested lands to Canadian citizens.
While the primary intent of the 1912 Forest Act had been to
belatedly halt the all-out assault of American capital on BC
timber, as a side effect it also prevented the disenfranchised
Punjabis from investing in logging companies of their own.
The 1907 law, however, remained in effect for forty years,
continuing to exclude them not only from creating their
own logging companies during that time but also from holding public office or practising in skilled professions such as
law and pharmacy.

Much more devastating at the time was an order-in-council issued by the Canadian government on January 8, 1908. This order, which required that immigrants must come to Canada by a continuous journey from the country of their birth or citizenship, was specifically intended to put a complete stop to all immigration from India, since at this time there was no direct passage available from India to Canada. And just to make sure that immigration was halted, the order also required that persons from India must have in their possession the enormous sum of two hundred dollars, although immigrants from Europe needed only twenty-five dollars. The effect was dramatic: between 1908 and 1914, only 117 immigrants were allowed to enter Canada from India.

The first significant challenge to this order-in-council occurred in November 1913 when 38 Punjabi Sikhs who attempted to enter the country were ordered deported; when their case went to court, however, the judge ruled that the continuous journey regulation was inconsistent with the wording of the Immigration Act, and they were allowed to stay. The second challenge came in the spring of 1914 when a wealthy Sikh named Gurdit Singh contracted the 3,000-ton steamship *Komagata Maru*, owned by a small Japanese cargo shipping company, to take a group of 376 potential immigrants to Vancouver. Half of the passengers had been waiting months—and a few of them years—in Hong Kong to make the journey, but the ship also stopped in Shanghai and the Japanese ports of Moji and Yokohama to take on others who had travelled there via regular liner from India to be part of the expedition. Of the total who embarked for Vancouver, 337 were Sikhs, 27 were Muslims and 12 were Hindus; only 2 passengers were women and 4 were children. All of them came from the central Punjab and nearly all were from elite land-owning families.

Those setting out on the *Komagata Maru* believed that Canadian courts would once again intercede, but by the time the ship left Yokohama, the Canadian government's "continuous journey" legislation had been rewritten to conform to the Act, and when the ship arrived in Vancouver on May 23, none of the passengers were allowed ashore. The standoff continued for two long months, during which time the police even blocked the re-provisioning of the ship. In early July when the justices of the BC Court of Appeal finally heard the case, they ruled that no principle in Canadian or British law gave the passengers the right of entry. After the government threatened to blow the ship out of the water if it failed to leave, it was escorted out of Vancouver harbour by the 3,700-ton cruiser HMCS *Rainbow* on July 23; it stopped in Japan to disembark some of the passengers and reached Calcutta on September 29. The returning passengers had hoped to incite the Sikh troops stationed in Calcutta to riot in protest over what had happened to them, but by this time the First World War had begun, and to avoid trouble from the *Komagata Maru*'s passengers, the viceroy's government had arranged for a train to meet the ship and take the returnees directly back to Punjab. In the clash with police who tried to force them onto the train, twenty of the returnees were killed.

Sikhs and other immigrants aboard the *Komagata Maru* were denied entry into Canada after arriving in Vancouver. The standoff lasted months before the ship was forced to turn around with all its passengers still on board. *Frank Leonard photo, Vancouver Public Library 5781*

Over the next five years, only one Indian citizen gained entry into Canada, while at the same time the Punjabi Sikh population of British Columbia shrank from a high of more than five thousand to just seven hundred persons.[2] Many had left for the United States, where the laws were less restrictive and the climate kinder, but some of those who left the country had returned to India, having achieved their goal of raising money for family land purchases. Others, incensed by the *Komagata Maru* incident, went home to India with the intention of stirring up a rebellion that would put an end to British rule there. A number, however, made the long trip home to visit families or get married, then found it impossible to gain re-admittance to Canada because they could not prove their earlier residency; their experience was enough to discourage Partap Singh Johal from making the journey.

CHAPTER TWO

The Lean Years

The *Komagata Maru* incident discouraged many in BC's Punjabi Sikh population, but for others it was just one more injustice to be confronted. As British subjects, they had a right to be in Canada and they were determined to prove it. They rallied together as a community, using their temples, or *gurdwaras*, as headquarters for strengthening their religious devotion while at the same time combatting government injustice with legal challenges. In 1919 their collective efforts paid off when restrictions were finally lifted on family reunification and at last the wives and children of the men already residing in Canada were allowed to enter the country. Immigration was a very slow process, however, with the first families only admitted more than a year later.

Meanwhile, employment in the sawmills in the Fernie area, which had reached a high of fifteen hundred workers in 1914, had shrunk to no more than a hundred workers by 1919 as all the easily accessible timber had been harvested.

Partap Singh Johal, who was now forty years old, was one of those who lost his job during those years. He picked up work wherever he could find it, finally returning to Vancouver, where he secured a lumber contract with the McNair Fraser Lumber Company in Marpole, an area that was at that time part of the municipality of Point Grey, not Vancouver. Robert McNair's sawmill was at 8961 Shaughnessy Street, an address that is just east of the present-day Oak Street Bridge off-ramp. "McNair produced bevel siding and cedar boards," Partap's son Asa explains, "and most of my father's short-term contracts with the company were for pulling lumber off the green chain and stacking it in the sawmill yards. But after a considerable time, he was given a contract to hire other Sikhs for the same kind of work in McNair's mill."

While working for McNair, Partap became aware that Sikh men who went back to India to visit their families were finding it less difficult to re-enter Canada, and in 1919 he returned to his home village of Jandiala in Punjab province to see his family. A year after his arrival there, he married fifteen-year-old Tej Kaur, who came from the village of Mulwha in the district of Sangrur, and their first son, Asa, was born on August 17, 1922. Partap, his wife and son lived on his family's farm, but though they were welcome there, he became determined to return to Canada; it took another year and a half after their son's birth for him to convince Tej Kaur to make the journey to such a distant country.

"After my father brought my mother and me to Canada in early 1924," Asa recalls, "he secured another lumber

Asa was brought to Canada when he was just a toddler.

contract with the McNair Fraser Lumber Company in Marpole." Asa's memories of his parents in those early years in Vancouver remain clear. He remembers his father as tall and thin, while his mother was short and plump, light complexioned with a round face and dark brown eyes, and she wore her long hair in a bun. A practical woman, she quickly recognized that it was in her best interests not to draw negative attention to herself in this new country, and instead of wearing Indian saris and Punjabi suits, she wore western garb—simple skirts, sweaters, blouses and pleated dresses. She made sure her husband dressed in Canadian fashion as well. According to her son, she was always serious-looking and "different from the handful of other immigrant women as she was strong-willed, driven, but kind-hearted and very social." Although she could be soft and gentle, she could also be tough and aggressive, especially in her home. In the tradition of her people, her life was dominated by her husband's life, but Partap deferred to her for everything, never questioning or arguing with her but more or less complying with her wishes.

Much of Tej Kaur's time was taken up with her children. She had given birth to Asa's sister Aussie in 1925, just a year after arriving in Vancouver; Prakash was born in 1927, Mary in 1928. By the summer of 1929, the family of six was renting a little house owned by a Japanese couple on Hudson Street in the Marpole area when Partap's boss, Robert McNair, offered him an unused four-room bunkhouse that was located next to his sawmill. It wasn't long after they moved in, however, that the bunkhouse also became a temporary residence for the numerous immigrant Sikh men who came to work for McNair, so that at times there would be as many as a dozen people living there. Tej Kaur, believing that it was her responsibility to look after them as well as her growing family, helped cook their meals in the adjoining cookhouse, and after dinner while she cleaned up, Partap and the other workers would linger at the table to have discussions.

It wasn't long before Partap felt the need for more privacy for his family, and he decided that he must buy a home for them. This was not a simple matter of approaching a bank for a mortgage, as the city's banks did not loan money to Asian immigrants. Instead, the members of the Sikh community had begun pooling their money, then loaning it out

Tej Kaur and Partap Johal sought to blend into Canadian culture rather than draw attention by standing out. *Frank Leonard photo, Vancouver Public Library 6232*

to their countrymen to buy land and homes. And this was how Partap was able to borrow money to buy a home on Logan Street, about five blocks east of the mill. Tej Kaur gave birth to two more boys after Partap bought the Logan Street house—Honey in 1930 and Mohinder in 1934.

In 1928 Asa began attending classes in a small brick school on Hudson Street in Marpole, but it was a lonely experience as most of the students were the children of Japanese mill workers, and he was the only South Asian. He recalls that "they mostly spoke Japanese, not English," so it was difficult for him to interact with them or to learn English. He did try to make friends with them, however, and his sister Aussie recalls, "Our father would give us money for candy, and we would go to the local store and invite all the Japanese kids in our neighbourhood to come with us and buy them candy because their parents couldn't afford it." When Partap found out what they were doing, he cut off their candy allowance.

According to Aussie, "Asa was a loner most of his life, and as a young boy he never played sports as the other children did." And Asa remembers himself as "a quiet, shy boy. I would take my time just walking along the railroad tracks to get to school ... What got me through school was math. What took the other students half an hour I did in ten minutes." But because he was slow to learn English, he was often kept back after the bell rang at 3:00 p.m. and made to redo his English reading, writing and grammar lessons. When Asa was eight, Partap, unhappy with the boy's progress, took

Asa and his brothers pose for a photo. Clockwise from top left: Asa, Gurdaas (Honey), Mohinder (Pete), Joginder (Joe).

him out of school, but since attendance was compulsory at that time for all children from age seven to fourteen, Partap's friends encouraged him to enrol the boy in a Vancouver school where the majority of the children spoke English. Fortunately, Point Grey Municipality had become part of the City of Vancouver in 1929, and after Robert McNair talked to somebody at the Vancouver School Board, Asa was allowed to enrol as a grade three student at the almost-new David Lloyd George School at Cartier Street and 67th Avenue.

Although it was a little farther for Asa to walk, Partap was pleased because the boy could now make better progress. For Asa the move wasn't as pleasant because he was bullied by some of the white kids at his new school. "They would make fun of me," Asa recalls, "and not include me in school activities." He was partway through his first school year there when he realized that all these kids were dressed far better than he was. He would stare at their beautiful clothes, wishing that someday he could own a pair of shiny new boots or clothes without holes, but at this point he could only dream, as his family was just scraping by.

There was also much sadness in the house on Logan Street as Prakash had developed tuberculosis and died at just four years of age on July 9, 1931. This little brother had always been different, Asa recalls. "He was born religious and talked about the gurus and wanted to see the *baba* [priest] at the *gurdwara* all the time. And after work my dad would take him in his wood truck and drive him down to the Second Avenue *gurdwara*."

Then one day in 1934 Asa came home from school and found his parents weeping. Mohinder, just six months old, had died from pneumonia. "My mother and father were barely coping with Prakash's death when a few years later, they would have to grieve the death of Mohinder. Both of my brothers had been ill for months, and it had been hard to watch them deteriorate, but their deaths didn't impact me as much as they did my parents because I was so young myself."

But there were more troubles ahead for Partap Johal and his family. By 1933 Canada was in the tight grip of the Great Depression, and the four western provinces, which relied most heavily on the export of raw materials and agricultural products, were hardest hit. The opening of the Panama Canal back in 1914 had sparked the growth of BC exports, especially lumber, and by the 1920s, ships had been leaving Vancouver with as much as 24 million board feet of lumber per year; with the onset of the Depression, those exports had been suddenly halved. Men whose average annual earnings had hit a high of $600 in 1929 now earned an average of just $353, and thousands upon thousands of them had lost their jobs; among BC's trade union members, the unemployment rate had gone from 2.6 per cent in June 1929 to 26 per cent in December 1932.

There was little work to be had at any of Vancouver's sawmills, and Partap was having difficulty feeding his family while paying off the loan he had taken out to buy the house on Logan Street, and when he finally couldn't pay, he lost the house. In an attempt to help him, Robert McNair offered to return the performance bond that Partap had deposited with him when he took on the contract to provide McNair's company with temporary workers. But Partap, not understanding that McNair was on the brink of insolvency, declined the offer, and thus he lost even those funds when McNair's sawmill company collapsed a few months later.

Partap found a rundown shack in the lower Capilano area of North Vancouver—it probably belonged to McNair as he still had a mill there—for his family and then a few months later uprooted them all again and moved them to the community of Alta Lake, which is now part of the resort municipality of Whistler. To get there, the family took a ferry north to Squamish, then travelled north again aboard the Pacific Great Eastern Railway. (The PGE—often known as the Please Go Easy or Prince George Eventually—was not completed to North Vancouver until 1956.) At Alta Lake, Partap bought a portable sawmill with the intention of supporting his family by cutting lumber out in the bush. He hired four Punjabi men to work with him, two sawyers to fell the trees and buck them to lumber lengths and two axe-men to de-limb the trees and pile the lumber. The sawmill, which had a fixed circular blade and a movable carriage, could only handle small dimension logs, so the set-up was not designed for high production.

The desolate, one-room clapboard house Partap had found for his family had no running water and no electricity, and it was surrounded by thick forests populated by bears and cougars. Asa recalls going to the outhouse at night by candlelight, and his sister Aussie remembers how hard it was for the family to keep warm. "It was such a terrible life and we were always cold." Adding to the children's misery, they had to trek through knee-high snow to get to the little schoolhouse. Asa, who was now twelve years old and in grade six, recalls, "The school at Alta Lake went from grade one to twelve, and we had one teacher who taught all of the ten students who attended."

The family had also taken in two boys whose mother had died and whose father had been admitted to Essondale Hospital, where he too had died. Asa became close friends with the older boy, who was also twelve. "His name was Gauchie, but he called himself Chick Burns." After school they would make slingshots and play together in the bush, but Gauchie was much tougher than Asa and got into fistfights at school. To keep him busy and away from Gauchie, Partap ordered Asa to spend his weekends and after-school time loading lumber for him, a job he hated, but it gave the boy an opportunity to see his father's milling operation up close and think deeply about it. He decided there was something thoroughly wrong with the set-up, but he didn't dare question Partap about it. Then one day it dawned on him that it didn't make financial sense to take the mill to the trees. It would be far better to build a stationary mill, and he began to dream of owning his own mill one day. "I guess when my dad had the portable mill up at Alta Lake, I decided I wanted to be in the mill business. That's what inspired me."

Meanwhile, Asa's mother complained bitterly about the appalling conditions the family was living in. She hated being alone there with no other women and she hated the two feet of snow. Partap tried ignoring her complaints, but according to Aussie, their mother didn't last a month there. One day she packed up most of their belongings and took Aussie, Honey and Mary back to the city. There they moved in with friends who had a house at Dominion Mills at the corner of Boundary Road and Marine Drive, the present location of Canadian White Pine Ltd. "We were so glad to leave that house at Alta Lake," Aussie says, "and the bears along with it."

Asa was left behind with his father, and for several more months they stayed on in the clapboard house in the bush. Then as the Depression deepened and there was less and less demand for lumber, Partap was at last forced to close down his mill, end his contract with the four men he had hired, and return with Asa to Vancouver to begin the search for work once again. When that proved fruitless, he borrowed enough money to buy a house at First Avenue and Burrard for his family and a truck so that he could go from house to house selling mill ends for firewood. That business lasted no more than six months, as so many other Sikhs were already selling firewood. This failure finally convinced Partap to give up on the idea of owning his own business.

In 1936, after Partap also lost the house at First and Burrard, he moved his family to a rental apartment at Second Avenue and Columbia Street in New Westminster and began the search for work there. "We stayed there for a while," Asa recalls, "and I would walk three miles [five kilometres] each day along the railroad tracks [the BC Electric interurban line] to Mount Pleasant School at Broadway and Kingsway." But it wasn't long before Partap decided that, since Asa was now fourteen, he should quit school and get a job. "I only studied up to grade six," Asa recalls with regret. "That was all the schooling my family could afford because it was hard for them to buy school supplies and clothes for all of us."

Partap found a job on the green chain at the Canadian Western Lumber Company—generally known as Fraser Mills—the largest sawmill in the British Commonwealth. It was located on the north bank of the Fraser River between New Westminster and Port Coquitlam, and employed over fifteen hundred workers, many of them Chinese, Japanese and East Indian, each nationality housed in separate bunkhouses. This was also where Asa got his first job as a spare maintenance clean-up man, working the eight-hour night shift six days a week and living with eighteen other East Indian employees in a company bunkhouse where he paid seven dollars a month for groceries. "I started working there for twenty-five cents an hour, though it was well-known that the non-immigrant white workers were getting ten cents more for the same work." With Asa and Partap's combined earnings, they were able to buy 10 acres (4 hectares) with a house on it in Queensborough. "I think we paid something like a thousand dollars for that property. We couldn't afford to buy it with cash, so we made monthly payments on it." It was in this house in 1938 that Tej Kaur gave birth to another

Partap and Asa both found jobs working for Canadian Western Lumber
Company, the largest sawmill in the British Commonwealth at the time.

son, Pete, who was sixteen years younger than Asa. (One
more son, Joe, was born to Partap and Tej Kaur in 1942.)

Around this time, Asa's sister Mary became engaged to
the son of one of the foremen at Fraser Mills, and when this
foreman learned that Asa was still handing his pay package over to his mother, he implored him to stop. "He said
to me, 'You are crazy to hand your pay over to your mom.'"
When Asa got up the courage to announce that he would no
longer subsidize the family, his father was angry, but Asa
told him, "I'm not living at home, and you and Mother have
no control over me."

On September 10, 1939, when Canada declared war on Germany, Asa Johal was just seventeen years old, but he had already been working at Fraser Mills for three years. After a decade of faltering lumber sales, housing construction was suddenly booming, so his job at the mill was secure. He was still very much a loner, though he had made friends with another Fraser Mills employee named Jim Lee who was a bit older than he was. Lee was a grader, a job that involved sorting lumber according to species, grade and dimension, and whenever Asa needed to know anything about the jobs he was given, it was Jim he turned to. "He lived alone and cooked alone," Asa recalls. "I'm not sure if he owned his place or rented it. After I bought a car, I would pick him up and we'd go out to the theatre or for a drink" in one of the gender-segregated beer parlours on Granville Street.

Then in June 1940 the Canadian government passed the National Resources Mobilization Act, which required all men eighteen years and older to register for the army, although they would not be required to serve overseas. Asa was still a few months too young to be drafted when the act was passed, but his friend Lee had to register, and when he was called up, Asa, hoping to fill Lee's position, asked if he would introduce him to his night shift foreman. But the foreman said, "I can't do nothing for you. You have to see the superintendent." Asa approached the superintendent when he made his rounds that night. "I told him I was capable of doing Jim's grading job, but he just said no. That was his answer. So I said, 'I quit!' And he said, 'You can't quit! It's stated in the Resources Mobilization Act!'"

Most of the Sikh men in British Columbia were incensed when they received their army draft notices, as they were still not eligible for Canadian citizenship. Why should they go and fight in Canada's war, they asked, if they were denied voting rights in this country? Asa felt the same, and at the end of August 1940 when he received his draft notice, he made a phone call to Victoria to speak to Bunt Bains, his sister Aussie's husband. Bains sent his educated cousin, Mohan Singh, to attend Asa's draft board meeting with him. "Mohan took me to the place on Seymour Street where they talked to you about whether you could get out of being drafted into the war or not." Mohan pleaded that Asa was the sole breadwinner in his family and that drafting him would create a hardship for the entire family, and "somehow he managed to get me a six-month deferral. Then at Christmas time Mohan said to me, 'Let's go over to see that fellow at the draft board and give him a present.' So we went to his home where he was working in his garden, and we gave him the present, and we never heard back from him or the draft board again."

Although Asa was still working the night shift at Fraser Mills at this time, he had also started on his first business venture, Queensborough Fuels, a name he chose because he had gone back to living with his family in the house his wages had helped to buy in Queensborough. "I would go to the Sawarne Lumber Company on Mitchell Island in Richmond

In 1940, Asa had just turned eighteen when he first received his draft notice. However, with the help of his brother-in-law Bunt, he was able to avoid serving in the army.

every morning and pick out the Douglas fir trim ends from the waste conveyors at their planer mill. I would pay for those trims based on Sawarne's daily production and go out and sell them for firewood." He advertised in the *Vancouver Sun* and paid a girl who worked in a nearby grocery store twenty-five cents for every order she took over the phone. His deliveries took him all over Vancouver, Burnaby and New Westminster, but he had no complaints because he was earning roughly two hundred dollars a week from his new business, and that was significant money in 1940. Smiling, Asa recalls, "It was a small but significant start, and I grew it bigger as the years went on."

Asa's contract with Sawarne ended abruptly after six months as the company was sold to a new owner, and he had to go from sawmill to sawmill looking for a new source of firewood. This time he ended up with two suppliers: Robert McNair, who had started a new cedar sawmill on the river-front at the foot of Argyle Street, and Bridge Lumber on Mitchell Island. And when Bridge's owner saw how hard Asa worked, he offered him a part-time job in his mill, which Asa accepted. Starting in 1944, as well as continuing to build up Queensborough Fuels, Asa worked alongside his father part-time on the green chain at McNair Fraser Lumber Company on Argyle. When the war ended just a year later, the industry changed overnight, as there was now an unprecedented demand for lumber for housing.

CHAPTER THREE

Family

I n 1948 Asa's friend Karnail Johal asked him to go to India with him. "Karnail told me that ten people he knew were heading to India soon, and he asked me to come, too. He was after me to get married while we were there." By this time Asa was twenty-six years old, and though he had been casually dating white women, in his heart he knew he wanted to marry a girl from India. The trouble was that he also wanted to marry in Canada, but single Indian women were still barred from immigrating into the country. He decided to go to Victoria and talk it over with his brother-in-law Bunt, whom he could always count on for good advice. When Bunt agreed that this would be a good opportunity to find a bride, Asa arranged for his father and brother Honey to keep Queensborough Fuels running while he was gone.

As there were still no direct plane or passenger ship services between Vancouver and India, Asa took a bus to Los Angeles, where he embarked on an American President Line

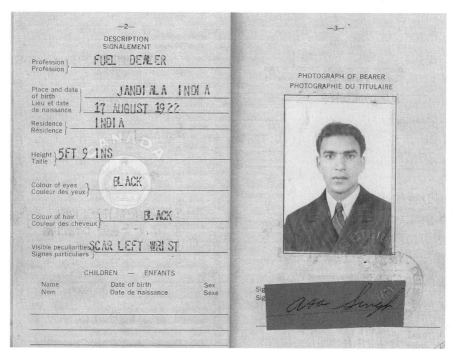

After casually dating for years, Asa returned to India to find an Indian bride.

ship to Hong Kong. Arriving there eighteen days later, he joined Karnail's group and boarded a plane to Calcutta. The train trip from there to his birth village of Jandiala in the province of Punjab exposed him to a culture and a language that were completely foreign to him, and when he arrived, he soon realized that the aunt and uncle he was meeting for the first time planned to use the traditional methods and customs to find him a bride.

Traditionally the parents of marriageable-aged daughters broadcast their intention to marry them off. The fact that there would be no dating, nor would the potential groom be allowed to see the bride until the day of the wedding presented problems for Asa. "I was not getting married to anyone unless I saw that person first! So my aunt and uncle asked the potential bride to ride by in a *tonga* (a horse and buggy) with her face just slightly covered so I could see her from a distance. I took one look at this lady and saw her body was built like a sumo wrestler, and I turned to my aunt and uncle and said, 'I can't marry her. She's not my type.'"

He explained that he would prefer to marry someone with a slender figure, and they agreed to continue the search for someone more to his liking. Meanwhile, his friend Karnail had gone to his wife's village of Bandala and spoken to a neighbour, Hans Raj Basi, whose sixteen-year-old daughter, Kashmir, seemed like a good candidate. But there was a problem: Asa was still adamant that he would not marry someone he could not meet or see, and Karnail knew that the Basi family would never understand this. Finally Asa capitulated and agreed that his aunt would go and see the girl, and if she reported back that the girl was good-looking and slender, he would consent to the marriage. He had to trust that his aunt would tell him the truth.

Kashmir Basi had been sent to live with her grandmother in a nearby village because the old woman was alone, and she was also being tutored at home because girls in the villages did not attend the local high schools; she was just finishing the eighth grade. She did not know that her family was preparing to marry her off, so when her mother arrived unexpectedly one evening, she was unprepared for her startling question: Would she agree to marry Karnail's friend from Canada? When she agreed, the next step was to meet with Asa's aunt to seek her approval. When they met, Asa's aunt explained that he had good prospects but at present he had few assets and not much money, and Kashmir would have to move to Canada, far from her family; the aunt did not explain that Asa was ten years older than she was.

Asa's aunt reported back that the girl was slender and pretty and that she and her family were lovely people. With the wedding date fast approaching, Asa became nervous. All he could think about was how little money he had. He had his wood delivery business and his job at Bridge Lumber several days a week to return to, but while he was in India, he had no money coming in. Being a sensible man, he phoned his brother-in-law in Victoria to ask if he would loan him enough money to pay for his and Kashmir's airfare back to Canada. He was confident he could repay it once he was home again. Even though finances were currently tight for Bunt and Aussie, they agreed.

Kashmir had little time to think about what she had agreed to and no time to get nervous. On her wedding day, December 7, 1948, when she finally met Asa, she realized that he was considerably older than she was, but as he seemed presentable, she decided she could live with that. Sohan Basi, her younger brother, recalls the wedding being a really lavish event. "Oh, it was a big wedding with at least maybe five or six hundred people attending or visiting our house in Bandala. My dad knew lots of people and his father, my grandfather, was well off, so people came from all the neighbouring villages to see my sister get married."

Meanwhile, communication between the bride and groom was awkward, as he knew very little Punjabi and she knew no English at all. "I remember when we were coming back to Canada," Asa recalls, "and we were going to board the plane out of Calcutta, and this Sikh Immigration fellow was speaking in Punjabi and I was answering him in English. Finally he looks up at me and says, 'What's the matter with you? Why don't you speak Punjabi?' And I said, 'Because I can't speak it properly!'"

Asa's parents were so anxious to meet their new daughter-in-law that they threw a party for the newlyweds on the day of their arrival in Vancouver via Seattle. But this party was held in the new house that Partap had built in Asa's six-month absence—a spacious, three-bedroom stuccoed house with a downstairs suite on a 10-acre (4-hectare) parcel of land on Mitchell Island, the long, narrow island that lies in the north arm of the Fraser River between Richmond and Vancouver and is today accessed via the Knight Street Bridge. By 1948 standards, the new house was very fancy, but the move came as a shock to Asa because he had contributed financially to the Queensborough house. It wasn't the right time to demand answers, however, because Partap Singh and Tej Kaur had put out their good china and invited the whole family and a few friends to the celebration. As Asa and Kashmir sat in the living room, he introduced her to his

Asa and his new wife, Kashmir, are pictured here just after their wedding.
The couple had difficulty communicating with each other in the beginning,
as Asa knew very little Punjabi and Kashmir spoke very little English.

brothers—Honey, Pete and six-year-old Joe, who all lived
with their parents—and his sisters, Aussie and Mary.

Kashmir soon discovered that Tej Kaur had a massive
presence whether she was in the home or not, and everyone
did whatever her mother-in-law wanted, but as her husband
loved and cherished his mother, she became determined to
please her, too. But while Sikh culture demanded that Asa
and Kashmir live with his family for the remainder of their
lives, Kashmir had not been prepared for her mother-in-law
to put her to work taking care of the entire household, preparing meals, cleaning and ironing, and she resented being

expected to make lunches whenever her mother-in-law entertained her friends and sat around chatting with them.

Meanwhile, Asa had thrown himself back into the lumber business, working at Bridge Lumber on Mitchell Island during the day and taking on extra shifts as an edger operator at Sohan Gill's Yukon Lumber at night as well as resuming control of Queensborough Fuels. Even so, he was aware of the enormous pressures growing inside the house on Mitchell Island. His mother's constant badgering was irritating Kashmir, and the tensions between himself and his father were escalating. He recalls, "Small problems began to rise between my father and me, and things went rapidly downhill from there."

The tension came to a head when Asa finally asked the question that had been on his mind since he returned from India: What had happened to his half ownership of the house and 10 acres (4 hectares) of land in Queensborough? His father ignored the question, but Asa persisted and finally Partap told him that he had made Asa's brother Honey forge his signature on the sales contract. Asa was very angry with his father. "I told him I wanted half the money from the Queensborough property or half of the new Mitchell Island property, and he refused to give it to me. Aussie and Bunt stepped in to resolve the dispute, and in the end I had to give my father $5,000 for an acre and a half of [the Mitchell Island river frontage] without a house. My father kept the rest of the property. I had to borrow another $500 from Aussie and Bunt to pay my father off."

Asa never held a grudge against his brother Honey for forging his signature, as he knew their father would have concocted some story to explain why he had to do it. But he soon found out that Partap and Honey had also taken over ownership of Queensborough Fuels while he was in India. Although Honey was now working at Hillcrest Lumber Co. on Vancouver Island during the week, Partap had him coming back to drive a firewood truck for Queensborough Fuels on the weekends. Asa was humiliated, but he was tired of being manipulated by his father and he chose to take the high road. He started a new company, Pioneer Fuels, and began buying peeler cores—the small-diameter poles left over after logs have been peeled for plywood—and selling them as firewood.

It came as no surprise to Asa when one evening in 1950, Partap took him aside and told him he wanted him and his wife out of his house. Kashmir was pregnant with their first child, and Asa, though unwilling to upset her, decided that they would move out immediately. With nowhere to go, once again he phoned Aussie and Bunt, and they welcomed the young couple into their home in Victoria. Once Kashmir was settled there, Asa travelled back to Vancouver and moved in with his parents again while he built a two-room cabin on his share of the Mitchell Island property. In the two months he lived in his parents' house, he did not speak to his father. It was the beginning of a rift that would last until the end of Partap's life.

By now Asa had accumulated enough money to buy another acre and a half from his father for $10,000, and although he knew he was taking a risk building a home so close to his parents, he also knew he had an anxious pregnant wife waiting for him in Victoria, and this was the best he could do for now. When the cabin was finished, he brought Kashmir back from Victoria. She was thrilled to see their first home and didn't even object to the fact that the bathroom was an outhouse.

The birth of their son, Darcy, on July 24, 1950, touched Asa in a way he had never before experienced. "I was so happy that we had a healthy baby. It changed me. I never go overboard with affection, but I felt that I had to get on with life now. I worked six days a week, twelve hours a day, and I would just see my wife and child at night for dinner, and that was it." He was even happier when his daughter, Geven, was born in 1953 because now he had a son and a daughter and he felt that his "family was complete." He found it difficult to be nurturing to his children, however, because of his troubled relationship with his father. Asa never bothered to explain these things to his kids, relying instead on Kashmir to make them understand that their father was absent from their lives because he was working to ensure that the family would have a secure future. According to Darcy, he and his sister were raised with a lack of physical affection, but somehow they always knew they were loved. "My dad was a hard-working guy. He didn't have a lot of physical love in him to give to us, but he meant well. He's just not a lovey-dovey guy who hugged his children or told us 'I love you.' But in those days fathers weren't like the parents of today.

The births of his two children, Geven (left) and Darcy (right), were momentous occasions for Asa.

———————————

I learned to love from my mother and my maternal grandfather, Hans Raj. He used to show me affection."

Each person experiences their childhood encounters, actions and situations differently, but the main thing Geven recalls from her childhood was the love. "Love is not always in words. People can tell you a hundred times that they love you, but their actions don't match the words. Love is all the things that a parent does for a child no matter what else is going on in the world. My dad always trusted my mom to

Although Asa had difficulty expressing his affection toward his children, Geven and Darcy never once felt as if they were unloved.

———————

spend the money he gave her. He trusted her 100 per cent. There has never been a day that he questioned her on the trust issue. Love was no different. It was a trust. You felt the love in our home without anyone saying it. You didn't get touched, no. But I would sometimes get a look from my father, and that look said *I love you*. Same with my mother. Everything they did for us was to further the family."

———————

Pioneer Fuels thrived, becoming just as successful as Queensborough Fuels, so that Asa was soon able to add a kitchen and another bedroom to the house, and he bought all the original property from his father plus another 7 acres (3 hectares) nearby. But living on Mitchell Island right next to the river was neither easy nor safe for Kashmir and the children. The property was surrounded by a mix of agricultural and industrial land that mainly housed immigrant families and small sawmill businesses. The island was connected to the mainland by the old Fraser Street Bridge and to Richmond by the No. 5 Road Bridge, and there was also a railway bridge to the mainland that allowed the island sawmills to ship out the lumber they produced. But there were only train tracks and a single gravel road down the middle of the island, and the Fraser River itself wasn't a safe place for the kids to swim, as the currents were so strong that one could quickly be swept away. But as small children, Darcy and Geven didn't seem to notice these drawbacks, and they enjoyed the vibrant South Asian and Asian community around them and made many neighbourhood friends.

Kashmir, however, was very lonely and found life in this setting difficult. In an attempt to ease her loneliness, Asa employed her at Pioneer Fuels. She recalls that, "he paid me for answering his business phone for Pioneer Fuels when he wasn't available. At the time I didn't know any English, but I could pick up the phone and take down clients' names and phone numbers and give them to Asa. Then he would call them back and take their orders and deliver the firewood." But Kashmir was still missing her family, and in 1954 Asa invited her parents to join them in Canada; although her

After sensing his wife's loneliness, Asa arranged for her brother Sohan (top left) and her father, Hans (top right), to come to live with them in Canada.

mother chose to stay behind in India, her father, Hans Raj Basi, did come to live with them. The following year, when Partap moved Asa's mother and younger brothers to the new home he had bought at Marine Drive and Fraser Street in South Vancouver, Asa bought the big house his father had built on Mitchell Island. A few years later Hans Raj and Asa made a joint application to have Kashmir's nineteen-year-old brother, Sohan, come from India to join them there.

Asa was now working harder than ever to support his family, but he always made time for his children. Geven developed an especially strong bond with her father as she grew up, and when she was young he nicknamed her the "Queen of Sheba." She recalls, "Darcy and I really looked forward to Saturdays. My dad would take us all downtown for dinner and a movie. It was our family entertainment night. We would go to fashion shows and art festivals, music shows and the theatre because these were things my parents loved. When my father worked, he worked, but when he took time off for us, it was all about us. There isn't one western movie that I haven't seen because they are Dad's absolute favourites, but if we said we wanted to see *Beach Blanket Bingo*, he took us to see it. He really would always ask, 'What do you want to see?'"

Christmastime was unique in the Johal household in those years. Although their family life was normally governed by Indian culture, Christmas was celebrated with Western traditions, making it a magical time for the children. Geven recalls, "Darcy and I would wake up early, excited, and jump up and down until we woke our parents because the Christmas tree was full of gifts for us. We could hardly wait to open them. It didn't matter if our parents had money or they didn't have much money because the tree was always full of gifts. We always got everything we wanted and more. Mom also made us special breakfasts, and Christmas night we would share our Christmas turkey dinners with Dad's family and friends. My dad would ask my mom to buy for his entire family, and we would go to my dad's mother, my grandmother Tej Kaur's home, and then sometimes we used to go the Blue Boy Hotel at Marine Drive and Fraser where Dad's brother Honey would have a Christmas party with the whole family. It was a time filled with laughter and joy."

CHAPTER FOUR

The 1960s and Terminal Sawmills

E ven in the midst of building up Pioneer Fuels, Asa Johal had never forgotten his dream of establishing his own sawmill, an idea that had first captured his imagination when he watched his father make an unsuccessful bid to start a sawmilling operation at Alta Lake. Since then Asa had worked in sawmills as a green-chain puller, lumber grader, edger operator, truck driver, saw fitter, sales agent, log buyer and accountant, and by 1955 he was convinced he was ready to become a sawmill entrepreneur. By this time, supplies for his fuel-selling business were secure, as he had a contract to pick up peeler cores from Sawarne Lumber, an operation that was now running round-the-clock shifts six days a week. However, he believed his best route to starting a sawmilling business was to take on a partner, someone with whom he could develop a strategy and share the risks. He chose a man named Bruce (Jogender) Sengara, who had a contract for peeler cores with the plywood company

J.R. Murray Ltd. Asa had known Sengara for some time and liked and respected him, and after the two men became partners, they enlarged their fuel sales business by building a mill to cut studs from the peeler cores.

The partnership lasted almost five years, then one day Asa learned that Sengara had gone out on his own to get a contract for peeler cores with Evans Products on Annacis Island, and when Asa inquired, he discovered that Sengara had not put the contract in Pioneer Fuels's name but in the name of his own brother-in-law. The partnership was subsequently dissolved, and by 1960 the two men had gone their separate ways, with Sengara taking the entire Pioneer Fuels Company, the peeler core mill contract, the stud mill and the truck.

Asa was left with only a half-built sawmill on his Mitchell Island property, but although he was angry at having been betrayed yet again, he now understood he would have to go it alone if he wanted to be successful. With complete control of his own company, he could move at his own pace, taking carefully calculated risks while he worked out his course of action. Although he had never gone to business school or taken sales courses, he had learned how the industry worked through reading, studying the competition and carefully following the fluctuating markets and trends in the softwood industry. He didn't write down a business strategy for himself, but he was convinced the way to success was to increase his production volume slowly and create exceptional wood products.

First, however, he had to finish building the sawmill, and for that he needed money. He turned to his father-in-law, Hans Raj Basi, and brother-in-law Sohan Basi, borrowing $5,000 from each of them and giving them shares in his company in return. Over the next two years, he completed the mill and purchased a used gang saw in order to cut logs into wide planks and cants and an edger to cut them into dimensional lumber—2×4s, 2×6s and 2×12s. He named his new company Terminal Sawmills because the mill was located near a trucking terminal. "I did have other names in my mind," he recalls, "but Terminal was the name that kept persisting."

Terminal Sawmills started with only nine employees, which included both Asa's father-in-law and brother-in-law, although Sohan went to school in the day to learn English and only worked nights in the mill. Asa also employed his brother Honey, who had his own trucking company by this time, but while he was a good worker, he also drank as hard as he worked and associated with questionable people. He had married when very young and he and his wife, Jeeto, had three children, but the marriage had ended in divorce. Tej Kaur also convinced Asa to hire his brothers Pete and Joe; after a short stint at Terminal, Pete went to work for Canada Post, but Asa recalls that "one day he asked if he could come back to work for me. I said yes, and he did. He retired at age sixty-five from Terminal." By now Darcy was eleven years old, and he worked for his father by helping to clean up around the mill, move logs, cut firewood and load the truck that would deliver the lumber. He remembers his dad being very hands-on right from the beginning, coming in early to sharpen the saws, installing them in the gang saw and getting everything ready before the early shift arrived.

Asa was also thoroughly involved in the day-to-day manual labour at the sawmill, a place where there is always a high risk of injuries. Lumber processing requires workers to deal with heavy loads and assume awkward postures that can result in all sorts of physical damage, including soft tissue injuries, sprains, strains, lacerations, puncture wounds and hearing loss. Asa experienced a few of these injuries. "Once I twisted my ankle at work and had to wear ankle supports and a back brace. Then my friend Nirmal Deol brought a man from India over to my house, and that fellow gave me these exercises to do to strengthen my weak areas. Fifteen minutes in the morning and fifteen minutes at three o'clock—twice a day. I did them for twenty years, and they worked."

According to Darcy, his father was involved in a number of life-threatening events at the mill. On one occasion Asa had just pulled the pins out of a truckload of logs when the driver moved the truck forward and the load began to spill out. "And in 1959 my dad's overalls got stuck in a sprocket while he was trying to install it correctly. The device took the clothes right off his body. He came home with no clothes on. Because he is a strong guy, he got out. Otherwise, he would have been dead. Another time in 1960 the guys at the mill told me he was picking up veneer cores. He used to roll the cores onto a truck to make 2×4s out of them, but this time when he pulled the pins on the truck, they began to roll off, much like his first incident. The majority of the load fell on top of him. If the rest of the load had fallen on him, he would have been dead. Thankfully, somebody came along and saw him and helped lift the cores off his body."

Asa's biggest problem in the early 1960s was procuring logs for his mill. Historically, both harvesting rights and manufacturing capacity in the coastal region of BC's forest industry had been dominated by a few big companies—MacMillan Bloedel, Powell River, Rayonier, Crown Zellerbach and BC Forest Products—along with a few mid-sized companies, and they turned out 80 per cent of the province's timber products.[3] Although the industry was experiencing significant changes in the 1960s, both as a reaction to fluctuations in market conditions and to the innovative forest policy legislation being enacted by the Social Credit government, access to harvesting rights for small start-up companies like Terminal Sawmills had not improved very much. They still had to buy their logs from the big companies that owned the forest management licences (later known as tree farm licences), and these big companies wanted payment for their logs up front.

One of Asa's solutions to this problem was to sign a contract with Balfour Guthrie Ltd., a San Francisco-based marketing company formed by three Scotsmen back in 1869 to channel British investment money into Pacific Northwest enterprises; by the 1960s, one of their specialties had become buying and selling both logs and lumber. "The logs I milled belonged to Balfour Guthrie because I couldn't afford them," Asa recalls, "but our agreement was that I bought the logs from them and cut them into lumber, then sold the lumber back to them." At the same time, he was cutting hemlock and fir dimensional lumber and selling it through another marketing outfit, the East Asiatic Company, in the US and Asia. Sohan Basi recalls that for the most part these contracts ran smoothly, though there were some glitches. He remembers times when they weren't getting enough logs in, and times when the workers had to stand around waiting at the mill for the log boom. "Sometimes they came in late from the forest or the weather could be bad," delaying the arrival of the boom.

For Asa the most significant problem at this time was the profit share Balfour Guthrie was taking, and after a couple of years he began looking for another agent. Fortunately, about this time he was introduced to Don King, a partner in the lumber producer Commonwealth Pacific and an agent for lumber sales in both the US and Canada. Since housing starts in the US were ramping up at this time, the demand for BC softwood lumber was steadily increasing, and Asa was happy to sign on with King. He also induced King to buy into Terminal—five shares at $5,000 a share. Then just to make sure he had all his bases covered, he also hired a salesperson to push Terminal's products locally.

As his sawmilling company slowly forged ahead, Asa made both friends and enemies in the industry. He often attended forestry management meetings during these early years, and at one of these sessions he met Peter Bentley of Canadian Forest Industries (Canfor). Bentley, who had worked in a variety of jobs in the business founded by his father, "Poldi" Bentley, and who would later become Canfor's CEO, recalls, "Asa always made such good sense at these meetings, particularly the ones on labour and marketing. I also knew that he never stopped working and he had an outstanding work ethic." Robert Ankner, the CEO of Boston Cedar, a company that would become a major buyer of Asa's products, noted that most of the established lumber tycoons in BC didn't like Asa because he was independent and smarter than most businesspeople in the lumber industry. "The tycoons of the forest industry," Ankner recalls, "the presidents and vice-presidents from MacMillan Bloedel, Weldwood, BC Forest Products, Interfor, Delta Cedar—they would hang out at Vancouver's Terminal City Club, and behind Asa's back, this old boys' club always predicted his demise."

In the winter of 1960–61, just as everything was rolling along nicely at the mill, the family suffered a personal setback. Asa and Sohan had just finished their six-day shift at the mill and were downstairs in the family home changing out of their work clothes when the sawdust-burning furnace exploded.

Flames shot across the basement, but as the two men rushed around trying to put out the fire, their clothes caught fire. Fortunately, a neighbour, hearing the explosion and seeing the smoke, had called the fire department, but when Kashmir and the children arrived home from a shopping trip, flames were already bursting through the roof. Geven remembers, "My mom was frantic because we couldn't see my father and Uncle Sohan anywhere. The neighbour tried to calm Mom down, but she was so worried until she saw him and our uncle come running out of the burning house with nothing more than the clothes on their backs." Asa and Kashmir looked at each other in total disbelief. They had lost everything.

Fortunately they had insurance, and while reconstruction began, they lived with Asa's parents once again, though this was awkward as Asa and his father did not speak. After two months the tenants who had been renting Asa and Kashmir's first little home on Mitchell Island gave notice, and the family moved in there until their new house was finished. This time when they moved out of the little house, it became the Terminal Sawmills office.

Although Partap was now in his eighties and had officially retired, one day Asa's brother Honey asked Asa to hire the old man. "I didn't know it then," Asa recalls, "but my father had been working for Honey, who had his own truck and had been delivering lumber for me at the time, and he'd had my father picking up and loading the wood into his truck. When my wife saw him doing that, we were scared that he could fall or have a heart attack, so I told my brother that our father should stop working for him. My father became angry when he heard that, as he thought he was still so fit even in his eighties."

The long dispute between father and son seemed to soften somewhat after that, but the next time they spoke to one another was in 1964 at the Richmond General Hospital. Partap, now eighty-five years old, had suffered a heart attack and was on life support. When Asa walked into the hospital room, he was surprised by how incredibly fragile his father looked. He was shorter than Asa remembered him, and his hair was thin and trimmed close to his head, though he still had a beard. "I went to see him the same day I heard of the heart attack," Asa remembers. "He says to me, 'Go and look after your business.' He wasn't worried about himself."

The doctor treating Partap told Asa that the damage to his father's heart was extensive, and since his chances of surviving surgery were bleak, he should be taken off life support. Although Asa, as the eldest son, was expected to make that decision, he felt overwhelmed by the idea. He and his father had, after all, been estranged for fourteen years. "My wife and I couldn't say anything because we didn't have a relationship with him," Asa recalls, "so we got my brother Honey to tell the doctor to take it off. When my mother found out, she was sure swearing at Honey. 'You killed him!' she said. But he was going to die anyway." Partap died nineteen days after being admitted to the hospital. Asa, realizing that what had transpired between them no longer mattered, paid

Funeral Set For City Sikh Leader

Funeral service will be held Saturday at 10 a.m. for Partap Singh Johal, 86, a well-known and respected figure in Vancouver's Sikh community.

Mr. Johal died Tuesday in Richmond General Hospital after a short illness.

He came to British Columbia in 1906 with his wife, Tejkour, from the Punjab, and was largely responsible for building the first Sikh temple here at 1866 West Second.

It was his wish to see the construction of the new $500,000 Sikh temple at Ross and Marine, which is to begin shortly.

In 1954, he founded the Terminal Sawmill Ltd., of Richmond, and at his death was still active in the family business. His four sons are directors.

He is survived by his wife, of 8190 Chester; sons Gurdas and Joe, at home; Asa, of 510 West Forty-ninth; and Minder, of 785 Southeast Marine; two daughters, Ossie, of Victoria, and Mary, of 8125 Prince Albert; 11 grandchildren and three great-grandchildren.

Service will be held at Hamilton Mortuary, 3290 Fraser. Cremation will follow.

Partap died after suffering from a heart attack. Asa had managed to reconcile with his father shortly before then.

for the funeral. "We had the service at the *gurdwara* on Second Avenue in Vancouver. I looked after all the arrangements and costs, and then I donated a good sum of money to the church." Following Partap's death, Tej Kaur gave Asa $35,000 to invest in his mill. After a few years she asked him for the money back, hoping she had gained some interest on it.

While Asa's relationship with his father and brothers was always tense, he had a special bond with his sister Aussie, and he came to her aid in 1965 after she left her husband. "She had helped me many times when I was in a bind," Asa recalls. "Aussie and her husband, Bunt, were very close to me, and any time I had difficulty with my parents she would step in and try to help smooth things out." However, Bunt gradually became an alcoholic, making the lives of Aussie and their children very difficult, and Partap had encouraged her to leave him. After the separation, Asa provided her with free lumber to build a new home for herself and her children in Victoria. Over the years he also gave her extra money on her birthdays, and in later years she accompanied Asa and Kashmir on many of their travel adventures.

———————

Later, when Asa bought L&K, his lawyer suggested that he put all his companies under one umbrella and call the company Terminal Forest Products instead of Terminal Sawmills. Asa liked the idea and agreed to the change.

By the mid-1960s, although Terminal Forest Products had come through some bad times, Asa was beginning to enjoy financial stability, and in 1967 Kashmir announced that she was tired of living on mill property. She wanted a real home, one that was separate from Asa's work and far away from his mother and the rest of the family. Without telling her husband, she had saved all the money she had earned over the years working for Pioneer Fuels, and she now had $5,000 in the bank to put down on a new home. Asa agreed. "We bought a house at Cambie and 49th Avenue. I didn't really have the money, but miraculously Kashmir had saved $5,000, and we put that down on the house. It was on sale for $55,000, and I paid it off in two years." The Mitchell Island home was left vacant so that it could be loaned out to friends and relatives who needed a temporary place to stay rent-free.

The family's move to the house on Cambie Street allowed the children to attend better schools. Geven, who was fourteen at the time of the move, spent the next three years at York House, a private school, but graduated from Burnaby Central Secondary. Darcy, who was almost seventeen, attended Sir Winston Churchill Secondary, where he became an outstanding soccer, baseball and football player; to his regret, neither of his parents attended his practices or saw him play in any of his games. But he remembers, "When I was young, my dad used to take me to Vancouver Canadians baseball games at Nat Bailey Stadium. He liked baseball." After graduation Darcy went to work for his father. He had literally grown up in the lumber industry, learning every aspect of it by doing it, much as his father had, and he transitioned easily into working there full-time.

Kashmir was surprised when she started to receive marriage proposals for Darcy soon after he graduated from high school. Like all South Asian mothers, she knew that both of her children would someday have arranged marriages, and when the time was right, she could count on her extensive social network to make inquiries. However, at this point marriage was the furthest thing from her son's mind. Instead, Kashmir and her children wanted to travel to England, and in 1969 when Asa couldn't take the time to accompany them, they asked Kashmir's cousin Karmjeet Basi to go with them because he had lived in England for several years. While in London, they visited Karmjeet's friends, the Rana family, who lived in Twickenham. For seventeen-year-old Manjit Rana, who was already betrothed to a man from Canada that her family had chosen for her, the Johal family's visit was life-changing. She recalls that "after dinner, Kashmir said to my father, 'We are looking for a bride for Darcy.' I jumped in and said, 'There's a girl across the road from us.' I took Geven and Kashmir to see the girl because Kashmir indicated they wanted to see her before they showed her to Darcy ... We quickly returned because they said, 'No, that's not the type of girl we want for Darcy. He's not going to like her.' My father turned to Kashmir and said, 'You might as well tell us what kind of girl you are looking for.' And Kashmir said, 'Someone like your daughter.' Over the next few days, my father asked if I wanted to marry the Johal boy, and I said, 'Whatever you think is right is okay with me.'" Darcy and Manjit had only spent a few hours together, but both Kashmir and Geven thought Manjit would be the perfect match for him.

The Johal family returned to England in 1970 for the wedding. "It was a real windy day," Manjit recalls, "and the wind kept flying my sari all over the place. My updo was coming undone and I had to spray my hair repeatedly ... Darcy couldn't find his turban because he'd left it at my parents' house. There was a lot of chaos and confusion trying to get it to him, but somehow we managed to get to the *gurdwara* on time, where Karmjeet and all the friends of my family were waiting." The reality of the changes ahead for Manjit didn't become clear to her until she was on the plane bound for Canada. "Halfway through the flight, it occurred to me that I was leaving my family and going to a different

Darcy and Manjit were married in a surprising turn of events. The two met while the Johal family was on vacation in England. From left to right: Asa, Kashmir, Geven, Manjit, Darcy.

country and going to live with a family that I didn't know. All of a sudden I started crying. Darcy tried to pacify me by saying, "Don't worry. Everybody is very nice."

The enormity of marrying into a now-wealthy and well-established Sikh family did not fully hit Manjit until she landed in Vancouver, where she was introduced to the extended family. Her life was about to be transformed and changed in ways she could not have imagined. For one thing, she had always thought she would have a career, but when early in her marriage she was offered a job as an interpreter, Kashmir and Asa made it clear that they didn't want her to work outside the home and that they had the financial means to support her every need.

CHAPTER FIVE

Labour Troubles and Mill Expansion

B y the beginning of the 1970s it was the general con-
sensus within the industry that Asa Johal was
successful, but having experienced abject poverty in the
1930s, he was always waiting for disaster to strike again. His
anxiety was increased by the nature of the lumber industry itself. "The lumber market could go up and down like
a yo-yo," he remembers, "and you could lose 50 per cent
of your profits just like that. And the Canada/US exchange
rate was volatile. Then there was the increased use of wood
substitutes, building products that are not graded as lumber—
engineered wood, plywood, particleboard made from chips,
wood pellets, sawdust and wood shavings. And you have logs
and lumber that—regardless of what's happening in the
marketplace—you've got to keep moving."

One problem he was not anticipating came in 1972
when his workforce decided to join the International
Woodworkers of America (IWA). It was a change he certainly

didn't welcome. "I thought I was treating my people fairly," he recalls. "We were offering competitive wages and benefits, but we had been working a nine-hour day six days a week, and they didn't want that." Sohan Basi, who was a supervisor for Terminal by that time, tried to convince the workers they were getting a better deal the way they were. "When they got together in the yard, I said, 'Look, you guys, if you join the union, you are only going to work eight hours a day, not ten hours and no Saturdays, so think about how much money you are making now. You're getting all the benefits that union members get except you aren't paying union dues.'" But finally it came down to a choice of accepting the union or shutting down the mill, and Asa had to concede, but he told Sohan and Darcy to sign up with the union, too.

"The union was hard to accept at first," Asa said, "because I'd always been independent, but I cut out all the overtime and limited work to forty hours a week. But that led me to put in more automated machinery, and that increased my production by 50 per cent and made up for the lost man-hours. It also brought my operating costs down." And Sohan recalls that "in the early to mid-'70s Asa's sawmill was cutting more than any of the other mills, and after he installed a lumber bin sorter, he was cutting more than anyone else could in eight hours. Other mills at the time had more people working for them, yet were producing a lot less lumber than Terminal."

Around Christmas 1972 when Asa began looking for ways to expand his operation, he was approached by the two

Anderson brothers who cut dimension lumber in a mill at the foot of Ontario Street. Their mill was for sale for $750,000, they said, and when Asa agreed to buy it, the deal was brokered on a handshake with realtor John Fairburn. At that point Harbanse (Herb) Doman heard about it. Doman and his two brothers had followed their father into the logging industry on southern Vancouver Island in the 1940s, and by this time they had built sawmills in Ladysmith and Chemainus. Now they were ready to expand to the mainland, and when they learned of the Anderson brothers' deal with Asa, Doman approached Fairburn, who told him that Asa had offered $1.2 million for the mill; Doman offered $1.3 million, which the Anderson brothers were, of course, very happy to accept.

Asa was outraged at the betrayal and phoned Doman. "I swore at him then hung up on him," Asa recalls. "At the time we were both directors of the East Asiatic Trading Company [which marketed Terminal's fir and hemlock lumber and wood chips], and I quit being a director." Asa took some satisfaction from the fact that the following year when the Japanese lumber market crashed, Doman made a serious investment error. "Herb Doman bought out Pacific Forest Products even after the Royal Bank told him, 'Don't do it.' So as soon as he did that, the bank cut off his credit, and he had to beg and borrow money at double the going interest rates." Although Asa's usual philosophy after conflict with others in the industry was just to move on and forget about it, he and Doman continued to rub each other the wrong way in all the years to come.

Asa's next crisis came as the result of events half a world away. In October 1973, Egypt and Syria invaded Israel in an attempt to recover territory lost in their previous wars, and Israel fought back with the help of American weaponry. The war ended with a United Nations–led ceasefire, but in retaliation the Organization of the Petroleum Exporting Countries (OPEC) cut off oil exports to the US, and the price of oil in North America quadrupled in a matter of months. The resulting recession in the US meant a slow-down in every industry, but particularly in home construction, and as housing starts came to a standstill, the Canadian softwood lumber industry suffered.

To keep his mill running, Asa began selling off some of his inventory at lower prices. "I had bought logs and had lumber sitting around, and then the market dropped. I lost a lot of money, but I kept the mill running. You know, sometimes you have to swallow the loss." Darcy saw first-hand how difficult this time was for his father. "Only once in my father's life—in the '70s when the lumber market really dropped—have I ever seen him really stressed out about money and business. But otherwise, in my lifetime with my parents, they never lived thinking about their finances day and night."

———

In the midst of these difficult years at Terminal Forest Products, the Johal family had been growing. In 1972 a Sikh

matchmaker had called Kashmir to ask if she would be interested in meeting a handsome young university student as
a possible husband for Geven. The matchmaker explained
that Avtar Opal had been just five years old when he was
sent to Vancouver from India to live with his widowed aunt,
Jeeto Oujla, and her six children. He was now studying math-
ematics and computer sciences at The University of British
Columbia (UBC). When Geven agreed to meet him, Kashmir
invited him to their home. "There was no deep conversation,"
Geven recalls, but afterwards the two young people spoke on
the phone several times and Geven realized their value systems were similar. "When Avtar told me his parents—whom
he never lived with—resided in India, and I said that my
family was going on vacation to India—it would be Mom's
first trip back since she immigrated to Canada—he asked
me to meet his parents there because he was interested in
marrying me." That meeting took place, and both families
agreed that the two should marry. In December, after the
Johal family returned to Canada, the traditional engagement
ceremony was held with the male members of the bride's
family going to the groom's family home to bind the engagement. Asa gave a gold coin to Avtar to signify the family's
commitment. The following day the Western part of the
ceremony took place, with Avtar and his aunt's family par-
ticipating in Geven's ring ceremony at the Johals' 49th and
Cambie residence.

With the engagement parties over, Avtar wanted to
court his new fiancée, but Kashmir strongly disapproved

as this was not traditional. However, in the face of Geven's determination, she finally agreed to allow weekly dates. "On our first date Avtar took me to the movies," Geven says, "and we went to see *The Poseidon Adventure*. And I remember we held hands. It was exciting." They were married the following May in an extravagant ceremony at the Ross Street *gurdwara* in Vancouver. As Geven was their only daughter, this was Asa and Kashmir's only opportunity to hold a lavish wedding, and in true Sikh tradition they invited over a thousand guests, making it more or less a community event. They also spent an extraordinary amount of money on the reception for five hundred guests in the Dogwood Room at the Pacific National Exhibition, but at Geven's insistence, this was a blend of both Western and Punjabi cultural traditions, one of the first of its kind in Vancouver's Indian community.

After a few months of marriage, Geven told her parents that she wanted to work and contribute to her marriage since her new husband was still in university. As it happened, Asa had a vacancy for a receptionist at Terminal Sawmills, though being the boss's daughter didn't give her any guarantee of getting the job. "My dad insisted that I had to interview for the position, and I'd only get it if his CFO deemed me suitable and qualified. Thankfully, he thought I was suited and gave me the job." Shortly after that, Avtar, now three years into his computer sciences degree, asked his father-in-law for a part-time job in the mill, and Asa assigned him the task of greasing the sawmill equipment correctly and regularly. That's when Avtar discovered he had an

Geven and Avtar were married in 1973 with an extravagant wedding that blended both Western and Punjabi traditions. Over a thousand guests were invited, making it a community event.

aptitude for mechanical things and liked working with his hands more than studying computer sciences. When he decided he wanted to be an electrician, Asa enrolled him in an apprenticeship program, and he received his certification three years later. Asa was impressed with Avtar's work ethic and asked him to join the Terminal team in the parts purchasing department as well as working as the company's electrician, an important position because the pace of production depended on the mill equipment working correctly. Avtar would end up working for Asa for thirty years.

In March 1973, Darcy and Manjit's first child, a daughter they named Roop, was born, and Manjit became concerned that they should move to a home of their own since Kashmir had said that Asa "would be bothered by the baby crying." However, that was not the case. "After Roop arrived," Manjit recalls, "my mother-in-law would take on the responsibility for the 6:00 a.m. feeding and put Roop on their king-sized bed, and Roop would sleep between the two of them. Asa became so attached to her that he played with her and even changed her diapers."

Chartered accountant Wells Wilkinson started working for Terminal Sawmills as controller and chief financial officer in 1973. Asa, who had lost none of his own facility with numbers and still never used a calculator, appreciated Wilkinson's ability to calculate in the old-fashioned way, too, and Wilkinson soon became Asa's right-hand man. Over the years the two men became very close, often going for drinks after work. Avtar, however, recalls being a little intimidated by the new CFO, who had started work at Terminal just a few months before he did, but he quickly came to like and respect his father-in-law's new colleague. "He was a very interesting individual. At first I was a little scared of him because he seemed very strict and upright, and you couldn't tell if he was serious or joking. But he was very shrewd and the most honest person you could ever meet, and that's why Asa and Wells were so close." Robert Ankner of Boston Cedar says, "Wells Wilkinson was more than the CFO of Terminal Forest Products. He was a straight shooter and the most honourable man I ever met." (Wells Wilkinson worked full-time for Asa until 2008 when he died from cancer.)

Asa, along with his close-knit team of leaders, was now almost ready to make his vision of a sawmilling empire come alive, but there was one vital person still needed on that team—an engineer. He found him in Albert Kovlaske, who had been working for Doman Industries for ten years at the time Herb Doman scooped up the Anderson brothers' mill from under Asa's nose. "Herb Doman and Asa were always competitors, and I always had to hear about it when I worked for Doman," Albert recalls. "So when Asa was trying to buy the plant that Herb wanted, Herb flew us over on a helicopter so he could negotiate with the Andersons and he ended up buying the plant."

Asa had already heard about Albert Kovlaske's remarkable abilities as a mill engineer from Bert Gisborne, co-owner of a company called Industrial Mill Installations Ltd., so it was only a short time after the Anderson mill debacle that

From left to right: Wells Wilkinson, Asa Johal, Bill Sauder. Wells was one of Asa's closest friends and confidantes until his untimely death in 2008.

Albert received an invitation from Asa to tour his Terminal operations. Asa flew him over to Vancouver, and he was immediately impressed with Asa's knowledge of the business and how involved he was in the day-to-day operations of the mill. "Operations would all pile up, and Asa would say, 'Just give me a minute,' and he would go down there and clean up the engine room, putting the pieces through one behind the other. He could run every machine. Somebody was in trouble, and he'd clean it up and he'd say, 'Give me five minutes,' and he'd go down and talk to the operator. I mean, here you got a guy who owns the mill, and he goes in and changes the saws."

Earlier that year, having been thwarted in his attempt to buy the Anderson mill, Asa had bought the Burke Lumber Company, located at the south foot of Yukon Street, adjacent to the westernmost end of Mitchell Island. It was owned and operated by another duo of brothers who were custom-cutting green lumber for the Japanese market. Because the market had declined, however, when Asa offered them $1 million for their sawmill, they accepted. He renamed it Mainland Sawmills Ltd. and began upgrading the equipment to do custom-cutting there for anyone looking for the optimum return on their logs. (Today that mill is still custom-cutting Douglas fir, hemlock, red cedar, yellow cedar and spruce under the Terminal Forest Products umbrella, and it is one of the very few sawmills currently doing business on the Vancouver side of the Fraser River's North Arm.)

On the day Albert Kovlaske came for his tour of Asa's mills, Asa told him about some of the changes he wanted to implement in his Mainland plant, then offered him the job of managing the new plant at an excellent salary. Albert thought about it for a few days and then accepted the offer. He gave Doman a month's notice, but Doman wasn't going to let him go without a fight. He began wining and dining him, and he warned him that taking the job with Asa was a colossal mistake. "Of course he told me all the bad things that were going to happen to me. He said Asa was going to go broke because he didn't know what the hell he was doing." Then Doman

The Mainland operation was responsible for custom cutting logs for clients looking for the optimum return on them.

---

tried to entice him with more money, and when he still said he was going to accept Asa's offer, Doman demanded to know how much Asa was going to pay him and said he would match it. When Albert remained adamant about leaving, Doman offered him a $30,000 annual raise. But Albert Kovlaske had made his choice. Afterwards he was never sure if Asa had hired him in an attempt to get back at Doman for stealing the Anderson mill, but he wasn't bothered by that.

Albert and Asa shared a similar past, which helped them understand each other. Albert had grown up in rural Manitoba, where the value of hard work and sacrifice had been instilled into him at a very young age. He had only managed to get a grade five education, and left home when he was twelve, eventually finding his way to BC. At seventeen he got a job at the Tahsis sawmill, and by the time he was eighteen he was already employed as a supervisor. Like Asa, he would end up taking care of his parents financially.

Asa tasked Albert with whipping the newly acquired Mainland Sawmills into shape because he was convinced it could make money if it was refitted with new machinery. But it required a lot of work and attention, and the two men would meet daily either at the plant itself or at Asa's house over a glass or two of rye whiskey, re-examining and re-analyzing the company's tactics again and again to safeguard against financial loss during the rebuilding process. One of Albert's first modifications was to enlarge the chipper mouth infeeds at both the Terminal and Mainland sawmills because they would often jam up, but in time he completely rebuilt Mainland Sawmills into the modern sawmill that was still in operation as of the time of writing.

Both Asa and Albert knew that the key to a successful sawmill is its capacity to cut logs into lumber quickly, consistently and with as little waste as possible. Logs come in one end of a sawmill and are debarked, cut to length, cut on a main head rig, edged, gang sawed, trimmed, graded, sorted by size and grade and stacked for further manufacture. Asa had been a leader in introducing innovative ideas to maximize production by picking out areas where he thought it was possible to increase his production and improve the quality of lumber. One of his very early upgrades at Terminal Sawmills had been the replacement of the large log-sash gang saw, which had a number of parallel saw blades bolted together to saw through the logs vertically to produce planks. When this gang saw fell apart, he had replaced it with a head saw and carriage assembly consisting of a top arbor saw and bottom arbor saw. A Trojan carriage was installed on tracks that could move the logs through the head saw assembly, and the carriage was moved along the tracks by a steel wire cable system powered by a Salem drive, with the logs held in place on the carriage by pneumatic clamping dogs. The log could be advanced toward the head saws on the carriage by an electric setworks that set the exact size of the slab to be cut, and the log could be rotated on the carriage by pneumatic log turners. The head sawyer controlled the complete operation of all this equipment from a soundproof booth, setting the size of lumber and cants (the partly processed logs with at least one flat side) produced from each log. The speed of this new equipment resulted in a tremendous increase in production and therefore an increase in the value of the lumber produced because specific lengths of finished boards are preferred.

In the next stage, the side boards from the head saw were conveyed to the edger. The uneven edges of the wide boards were ripped by the multi-saw edger with its shifting saws to make sized boards with parallel sides. These cants, which could be from 4 to 12 inches (10–30 cm) in thickness and up to 36 inches (91 cm) wide, were transferred to a double arbor gang saw, which could rip them to make as many boards as the spacing of the arbor saws allowed.

But when Albert came to work at Terminal, Asa counted on him to come up with fresh solutions to improve on this system, and in 1976 they made another mechanical upgrade by installing a Schurman double arbor gang saw, a machine that has two banks of saws on a shaft called a saw arbor. These saws are stacked one on top of the other, so a 12-inch (30-cm) cant of wood can be sent up from the head saw to make a number of 2-inch by 12-inch (5 by 30-cm) boards, the number depending on the width of the cant. The advantage of the Schurman saw was that it delivered so much more production per hour. When this installation at Terminal Sawmills proved its value, Albert installed one at Mainland Sawmills as well.

Albert often created full-size models of the new saw-mill equipment he was planning to build in order to identify design flaws and safety issues. Then he and Asa would go over the process together, which allowed Asa to identify potential problems. Albert recalls, "Asa would come and take a look at it and say, 'It works here, but how the hell do you know it's going to work there?' And I would say, 'Well, if it works here, it's going to work up there.' He was meticulous—I look at it like it's going to work, and he looks at it like what if it doesn't work? That's the way it's got to be. That's vision. Then Asa would say, 'Okay, if you really think it's going to work, then go ahead and build it.' He always had the final decision."

However, if Albert didn't like Asa's decision, it was up to him to convince him otherwise. Over the years they did disagree from time to time, but Albert says they rarely had major disagreements, and when they did, they always resolved their differences. "Disagreements are natural," he maintains. "They are inherent in business. If you work for somebody or somebody works for you, if you are going to be a total yes-man, then you are no good to them. If you believe in something that is going to work better, it is up to you to convince that person." Albert quickly developed respect for Asa. "He had one of the greatest visions that I know of. Whether it was a good idea or bad idea, he threw it out at you. We'd talk and say, 'That won't work, this won't work,' but he had a great vision. He was so thorough at what he did, but he also liked what he did. He was such a hard worker." This admiration went both ways, and Avtar Opal recalls Asa's high regard for Albert and felt it was partly because his work ethic was similar to his own. He remembers that Asa sometimes had Albert at the plant 24/7 to make sure things were installed and running correctly. "Albert was always tinkering with the models he designed. He would spend most of his time creating drawings and then constructing models of them. You cannot put in equipment that doesn't do what you want it to or you'll lose money and efficiency."

In his determination to modernize his mills, Asa also spent hours seeking out information about new sawmill technologies and travelling to look at the newest equipment. He took Albert with him on one of his trips to a mill equipment auction in Houston, Texas, and Albert remembers sitting on the plane next to him. "I was still pretty new to the company and I turned to Asa and asked, 'Did you bring a purchase order?' [When he didn't say anything,] I asked again, 'Did you bring a purchase order number? If we buy something, how do we pay for it?' Asa just smiled. 'Oh that's easy,' he said and pulled seventy $1,000 bills out of his pocket. Nervously I replied, 'Put that away. We are going to get into trouble.' Asa had always paid cash for everything, and he always paid his bills." However, when they returned from Texas, Albert swiftly implemented a purchase order system for the company.

The final important member in Asa's support team was banker Anant Pal Singh, an immigrant to Canada and the son of an Indian army general. Asa first met him through Darcy at a mutual friend's wedding reception then met him again in 1974. AP, as he was generally known, was the first South Asian manager in the entire Bank of Montreal system, and though Asa had already been dealing with that bank for both his business and personal banking when he met AP, becoming Asa's friend certainly helped AP's reputation there.

At first it was Darcy who invited AP and his wife, Surinder, to the Johal home as they were closer to his age, but they soon became like family.

AP was curious about the lumber industry, and from the beginning of their friendship he felt comfortable enough with Asa to ask him questions about it and in this way gained insight into the business. "I knew some of the bankers that Asa's companies were dealing with at the Bank of Montreal," AP recalls, "and they would talk about this Indian family that had a sawmill business and how well they were doing. By that time I had already met the family, so I knew who they were talking about. The bank had a lot of regard for this guy who was not that well-educated but really knew the lumber business, but for them, Asa Johal was just a small person because he only had a small operation. But I could see he was competing head-on with the big names like Canfor, Weyerhaeuser and Doman even though he had limited resources, and I found that quite fascinating."

On Saturdays, AP would often visit Asa at one of his sawmills. They would walk through the entire mill, and he was always impressed by how Asa knew precisely how each piece of lumber went from here to there and finally where it would end up on a truck to be shipped out. AP could see that Asa was always striving for better results and for higher production output. If his sawmills were producing twenty loads, Asa wanted to get thirty with the same labour and the same equipment. "He wanted to produce a far better product than anyone else could. And that's what drove him. I don't think

Asa (left) and Anant Pal Singh (right) boasted a close relationship and Asa considered him a part of his family. Anant Pal later became Asa's personal financial advisor.

he had any kind of role model to follow ... And for me, he became a role model." AP considered Asa to be honourable in every way and believed that if he gave someone his word, he would stick to it. AP said, "I remember telling the bank that they do not need any security from Mr. Johal, that as long as he has signed it and he has said yes, he will take care of it, that is all the bank needed. Of course, for the corporate side, it is a different story. You have to give all kinds of legal securities, but from the personal side, that is all the bank needed. He is honourable."

As their relationship flourished, AP became Asa's closest confidante and his personal financial advisor. In return, Asa opened many doors for AP, introducing him to other South Asian businessmen in a world that was dominated by non-South Asians. AP left the bank in 1994 and went out on his own as a financial advisor, providing advice to many billionaire clients, but his relationship with Asa remained personal and he regarded him as a father-like figure.

By the time the recession officially ended in March 1975, Asa had decided it was time to take some calculated risks to expand his company, but for the plan he had in mind to succeed he would need complete control. As Don King of Commonwealth Pacific still owned shares, he offered to buy them back at $50,000 a share, a nice profit on his purchase price of $5,000 a share. After King accepted the offer, Asa began putting all the money he had made back into the business and looking for ways to become even more efficient.

He had a relatively clear idea of where he wanted to go with his business by this time, but he knew another critical aspect of his future success was having access to the best logs in BC as well as an assured log inventory so he wouldn't waste time with an idle mill. He was buying some of his logs from BC Forest Products at this time and supplying that company's pulp mill at Crofton on Vancouver Island with hemlock and balsam chips, and as a result he came to know

BCFP's vice-president, Gerry Burch. "Mr. Tichi, who managed our chips and log supply," Burch recalls, "looked after
Asa and respected him a lot. We used to get custom cuts on
our log booms done at Mainland when we couldn't process
them in our own facilities. We were a tight-knit group on the
West Coast, and we had respect for one another. Asa was a
sharp businessman, and when you made a deal with him, he
honoured his word. He was smart enough to keep the dollars
coming in and thank god he survived."

Asa's practical solution to log buying had always been
to employ his own log buyers. The first was Bud Perry, who
worked for Terminal until 1975. He was followed by Robbie
Thurston. Avtar explains, "A log buyer physically goes out to
look at the logs on the ground or in the water and decides if
they are suitable for your production requirements, and he
negotiates the price the company is going to pay for them.
Robbie Thurston was good at his job, and he had a lot of
connections at Canfor and Interfor." As a result, Thurston
became very important in Terminal's next negotiations.

By the mid-1970s a strong demand for western red
cedar had developed in the eastern United States as well as
in Europe because of its excellent rot-resistant properties
and its usefulness as external house cladding and in situations where high-end finishes were needed. The demand
increased after 1968 when the US government passed legislation to protect the remaining redwood forests of California
and southern Oregon. As a replacement, the US construction industry turned to BC's western red cedar because it

had similar characteristics. To take advantage of this market, MacMillian Bloedel, Weldwood and Interfor had been gradually making the switch from Douglas fir and hemlock to cedar and gobbling up smaller sawmills and logging operations. Bill Sauder, who owned the controlling interest in Interfor, went on a buying frenzy and purchased twenty-five small and mid-size sawmills in BC as well as timber-cutting tenures and logging operations.

Terminal Sawmills was still cutting and selling hemlock and fir dimensional lumber at that time and marketing it through the East Asiatic Company to the US, Europe and Asia, but the company's financial returns were disappointing and switching to cedar just made financial sense. "The market was dead in Douglas fir," Avtar recalls, "and we were losing money cutting it, then somehow we acquired one boom of cedar, and it was, 'Okay, what are we going to do with this?' We cut those logs into 200,000 board feet of lumber and not only broke even on it but made a little bit of money. That's when Asa got the idea. That's when he made the change to cutting cedar." Some of these cedar logs were too big in diameter for the saws at the Terminal Sawmill to process, so they were re-routed to the Mainland Sawmill, where they were custom cut. Gerry Burch, former VP of BC Forest Products, thought Asa had made the right move. "It was very smart of Asa and an indication of his business acumen to switch over to cedar."

Asa was now closer to playing in the big leagues, and in 1975–76 he signed a fibre supply and sales agreement contract with Canfor, the company founded by "Poldi" Bentley and his brother-in-law, John G. Prentice, after they fled Nazi-occupied Austria in 1938. They had started with one small plywood plant on the Fraser River, but their company was now a major player with cedar holdings at Harrison Lake and Chehalis and other camps around the Lower Mainland. Darcy Johal speculates that the fact the Bentleys were also an immigrant family might have influenced them to sign the contract with Terminal. "Bill Dunbar, the salesperson for Canfor, was negotiating with three companies at the time, and we were one of them. Canfor's Inglewood logging division was already supplying Terminal with some cedar logs, and Bill knew Robbie Thurston, who was Dad's log buyer. So Jack McMillan, who was the sales manager for Canfor, and Bill Dunbar picked our company because he thought we were better operators than the competition. I think Bill told Poldi and [his son] Peter Bentley that my dad was the best guy to go forward with, but Dad also offered Canfor more commission than the competitors were offering. So that's how he got the contract." In fact, probably the two most important factors deciding who got the contract were Jack McMillan's appreciation of the quality of the cedar products that Terminal Forest Products was turning out and his long-standing relationship with Asa.

The fibre supply and sales agreement provided that Canfor would give Terminal first rights on high-grade cedar logs and purchase Terminal's cedar chips for its Howe Sound Pulp and Paper Mill. In addition, since Canfor didn't have a western red cedar line to sell, Terminal Forest Products would become their finished cedar products supplier. Terminal benefitted greatly by having the Canfor logo on their lumber, and Canfor, which had a large network of distributors strategically placed in the US, received a commission for selling it. This arrangement was mutually beneficial and remained in effect until 1997.

The size and grade of the logs determined where Asa sent them to be cut. The larger logs and higher grades would be cut at Mainland, while logs under 40 inches (102 cm) in diameter would be cut at Terminal. This lumber would be sold for cedar siding, panelling, trim boards and components for furniture. As with the fir and hemlock Terminal cut, the by-products—chips, shavings and hog fuel—were all sold to the pulp mills. Asa was happy with the switch to cedar and started looking around for other cedar log opportunities to energize his business.

———————————

Meanwhile, his private life was undergoing change. With the birth of his first grandchild and Darcy and Manjit's decision to continue living in the family home, they needed a larger house, and Asa found a suitable one on 55th Avenue. It was large enough that everyone could maintain their privacy, though Asa and Kashmir could continue to play an integral role in helping to raise the children; the challenge for Darcy and Manjit would be to preserve parental control over their kids.

Asa and Darcy's routine after their day at the mill would begin with a long shower, then Asa would pour himself a glass of rye whiskey on the rocks and settle into the armchair that had been a gift from Darcy, paid for by his first paycheque from the mill. It had now been reupholstered several times and gone with the family from house to house. Asa's granddaughter Roop remembers, "As soon as I heard the downstairs door, I would run downstairs and wait for my dad and grandpa to come in. They always smelled like cedar. After they took off their work clothes and showered, I would sit on my grandpa's shoulders, put a *chuni* [a long scarf] on his head and play the drums on his bald forehead and wait for him to finish his drink so I could suck the ice. It was a routine we did every day when I was a child." Although it could not have been pleasant to have someone pounding on his head, Asa never stopped her. Manjit and Darcy would have two more children while they lived in that house, their sons, Sanjay and Rummen.

In 1977, Geven and Avtar both remained employed by Geven's father at Terminal Sawmills, but they were expecting their first child. By now they could afford to move out of their one-bedroom Marpole flat, and they had saved enough money to build a house in Richmond, designed by architect Don Delinsky.

For holidays Asa was drawn to the warm climate of Palm Springs, California, and after two trips with his children and their partners, in December 1977 he bought a townhouse there. "The first property we looked at was an all-senior-citizens type of place," he recalls, "so we couldn't buy there because our grandkids are so noisy. Then we found a place they were just building, and this woman had bought twenty units there. She wanted $180,000, and I said okay and put $10,000 down, and then someone else came along and offered her more. So I bought the place next door for $10,000 more." It was a three-bedroom townhouse in a gated community with a shared common area and pool, and in the years to come Asa would use this new acquisition for entertaining and as a place to unwind and read, now one of his passions. He immersed himself fully in history, politics and biographies and would read newspapers from cover to cover.

CHAPTER SIX

Maximizing Efficiency

A sa Johal and Albert Kovlaske were always looking for ways to maximize the mill's efficiency with the least amount of by-product and waste. Starting in 1977 they concentrated their efforts on the issue of kerf, which primarily involves a sawblade's thickness and number of teeth. Decreasing the thickness sometimes means that the blade cannot maintain its stability and will begin to wobble during the cutting process, increasing the amount of wood pulled out of the sides of the cut, but in general the thinner the saw blade and the more teeth it has, the less wood is turned into sawdust as each log is passed through the mill, and the more boards emerge. "The ultimate goal of the sawmill owner," says Avtar, "is to have zero sawdust, so we kept making the kerfs thinner and thinner to get more usable wood. In the old days the kerfs were 0.375 of an inch [9.5 mm], but you just can't survive doing that anymore. We went from 0.25 down to 0.125 of an inch [6.35 to 3.2 mm], and my band saw's kerf

The maximum number of boards that can be obtained from a single log is affected by the thickness of the saw blade. Asa and Albert attempted to maximize efficiency by making the saw blades thinner, but that created another set of problems that needed to be resolved.

———

was 0.095 of an inch [2.4 mm], which meant if we had a wide enough piece of timber, we could get a whole extra board out of it. So we made all these things more efficient and got more recovery, and that's the name of the game. Logs cost so much money that you have to maximize the number of pieces of lumber you get out of them. It's all about grade and recovery."

However, complications arose as they thinned the saw blades, and Albert Kovlaske's next task was to design a guiding system that would hold these thin saws in place and prevent wobble. Asa was always excited by the enormous gains made with Albert's inventions, and Avtar comments, "Asa always wanted things better. If he could make anything better, he would."

Albert's next task was to design a better system to handle all the lumber that was exiting Terminal Sawmills. The heart of the new system was to be twenty lumber bins (later increased to fifty bins) and an end stacker, all of it supplied by Newnes Machinery of Salmon Arm, a company owned by Ray Newnes and his sons Doug and Bill, which had grown from a small blacksmith shop back in 1912 to become North America's leading manufacturer of fully automated sawmill equipment. The new equipment they supplied sorted the lumber into bins according to width, length, grade and thickness before the stacker took it from the bins to package it.

By this time Asa was cutting cedar exclusively in both of his mills and starting to make money, so it was time to make his next move: construction of a finishing or remanufacturing mill in Washington state that would produce high-end cedar products for sale there, thus avoiding countervailing duties and tariffs. In 1977, Asa took Albert Kovlaske on a series of trips across the border to look for a suitable mill site. "There was nothing there," Albert recalls, "but Asa just kept buying up equipment." At last he bought 40 acres (16 hectares) of industrial property in Ferndale,

Washington, but about this time he was reminded that the fibre supply and sales agreement he had signed with Canfor did not allow him to build and operate a US plant. Asa wasn't willing to give up on a plant there as a future project, and in the meantime he decided to use the Ferndale site to store the machinery that he had bought at auction. It remained there for the next year while he arranged for the construction of a rail spur onto the property so that at some future time, he could ship lumber there to make finished products for his US customers.

In spite of the setback on building his Ferndale mill, Asa hadn't given up on his plan to establish a remanufacturing plant to increase the value of his base products, but for now he would build that mill in Canada, and he had just made this decision in 1978 when a 5-acre (2-hectare) property at the foot of Ash Street came on the market. It was perfectly situated, just two blocks west of his Mainland Sawmill on a Canadian Pacific Railway siding, and it included a very old plywood door manufacturing plant, part of the extensive J.R. Murray group of businesses. It was a great find, and after Asa bought the property, he christened it Mitchell Island Forest Products, even though it was not on the island but on the mainland side of the Fraser's North Arm.

Asa had only one man in mind for managing the new plant: his son-in-law. But Avtar Opal was nervous about taking on such a big responsibility. When he protested that he didn't know anything about running a finishing plant, Asa told him he would learn as he went. Still feeling reluctant,

Avtar said that he had never run any kind of business before and was surprised when Asa said, "That's okay. We're all new at it, so that's no problem."

The new remanufacturing plant started out with just nineteen employees, and often they were responsible for multiple tasks. Avtar himself managed the plant while continuing to do all of the company's electrical work, act as purchasing agent, buy lubricants and bearings and do repairs on equipment. By now he and Asa had a good working relationship, and when Asa would come to him with his ideas, it was up to Avtar to try and make them happen. Avtar recalls, "Asa comes up and says, 'Maybe we should do this.' I say, 'Let me think of a way.'" If Avtar wasn't able to figure it out on his own, he turned to Albert Kovlaske for help. Fortunately, in 1979 Avtar learned that Asa's old log buyer Robbie Thurston was looking for employment once again. "Robbie had tried going out on his own in 1978 and when that didn't work out, Asa enticed him back and had him working with me at Ash Street as an assistant."

The next problem to be resolved was how to transport the lumber from Terminal Sawmills to the new remanufacturing plant, and Asa suggested that Geven and Avtar take on the contract. Avtar seized the opportunity, purchased a truck and trailer, and called his new company Opal Trucking. He hired a driver to shuttle loads of lumber between the two locations all day long. However, even though Geven and Avtar ran the company, Asa controlled it financially and made all the decisions, and according to Geven, although she and her husband ran the company for eighteen years, they made very little money from it.

Meanwhile, Asa had become determined to set up lumber-drying kilns to reduce the moisture content in his cedar products and prevent unnecessary shrinkage, thus maximizing his returns, but he didn't have space for kilns or room to store the dry lumber in any of his three facilities. Then by good luck a planer mill on an 18-acre (7.3-hectare) site adjacent to Terminal Sawmills on Mitchell Island became available. It was called Transco Mills, and the owner, Lou Berger, was having difficulties with his operation. "I always visited Lou around Christmas," Asa explains, "and that year he said, 'Why don't you buy my mill?' I asked him how much he wanted. 'Four and [a] half million dollars,' replied Lou. I said I would give him four million cash. He said, 'No, I want four and [a] half million.'" Asa knew Berger well enough to understand that he wasn't going to move from his asking price, and he bought the mill for $4.5 million. Now he had a place for his kilns as well as storage space for his dry lumber. But the Transco owner also had a smaller 4-acre (1.6-hectare) property on the north side of Mitchell Road and he offered it to Asa as well. "We needed the yard space, so it was good for that kind of expansion," Asa said. This deal increased Terminal Forest Products property from its original 4.5 acres (1.8 hectares) to more than 30 acres (12.1 hectares).

"We kept the planer mill at Transco but ripped out the old dry kilns and the scrag saw [used to saw short logs into two- or four-sided cants]," Avtar explains, "and we bought three new dry kilns for about a million and [a] half." Once the kilns had been installed at the new Terminal Planer Mill, Asa started drying lumber there and finishing it at the new remanufacturing plant on Ash Street. By finally owning all the stages of production, he could get more value out of his cedar logs, and according to Avtar, it was at this point that Terminal really became successful, in part because not everyone in this fiercely competitive business could control the whole process in this manner. Through expanding his product line, Asa was now able to offer his distributors a one-stop shop for all their cedar needs.

Asa now turned his attention back to the renovations needed in his newly purchased Mitchell Island Forest Products mill. His plan was to modify the 110,000-square-foot space so it could produce high-grade cedar bevel siding and kiln-dried products (as well as some green products) such as the channel siding used for home exteriors, tongue-and-groove panelling for home interiors, kiln-dried cedar trim boards and other patterned kiln-dried products. Once this cedar product line was perfected, he could also begin kiln-drying fir and hemlock, finishing it at Mitchell Island Forest Products and shipping container loads of it to the Japanese market.

Albert Kovlaske was given the job of making the necessary changes in the old building and installing new equipment: a moulder to make patterns for trim boards, a Stetson-Ross planer for dressing the wood and a tilting resaw for bevel siding. For the most part, Asa now trusted Avtar to

Asa expanded his product line to include finished products such as bevel siding, panelling and more. By owning all stages of production, Asa was able to become fiercely competitive within the industry.

deal with the mill's day-to-day operations. He would give him a general overview and vision of what he expected, only interfering if he disagreed with how something was going, particularly when it came to grading the lumber, as this had to be done with great care to get the highest value from each piece of cedar. Avtar recalls one occasion when the lumber wasn't graded correctly, and after it was kiln-dried, all the knots fell out, making the wood useless. "We had our own in-house graders, which was different from the industry standard because we knew which types would go into a particular finished product. If it had big knots and good wood in between, it would be a shop grade. Or if it was knot-free and fine-grained then it went into a clear grade."

Grading was particularly important in the forest industry, not only to get the highest value out of a board, but also to ensure that the board would be given the right treatment.

———————

To this end, he lured his uncle, Harjap Dhaliwal, away from Delta Cedar to work for Terminal Forest Products because he had grading experience with western red cedar. Dhaliwal became the supervisor in charge of training and operating in the new plant, and in later years became training and quality control supervisor at the remanufacturing plant that Asa finally built across the border. He remained working for Asa until he retired.

One of the products Mitchell Island Forest Products produced was cedar siding for houses, and the company had to train new planer men and technical people to carry out the company's unique way of processing the lumber. According to Avtar, the traditional method of grading siding had been to pass the piece longitudinally in front of the grader, who then transferred it to the appropriate sorting bin. But this was not a very efficient way to do it, and it was slow. "We added more lights and mirrors until the graders were able to see the entire length of the piece at one time," Avtar says. "Our other major problem was figuring out how to prevent damage to the board or siding after it exited the moulder, planer or resaw. We resolved this by installing specialized equipment such as tipple slides, UHMW [ultra-high molecular weight] plastics, chromed surfaces, rolls and non-marking special belts on all the transfers."

As Asa was making these changes to improve his company's cedar lumber output, he was coming into direct competition with International Forest Products, or Interfor, which was well on its way to becoming one of the largest lumber producers in the world. At this time Interfor was specifically striving to become the West Coast leader in cedar production, partly by acquiring other sawmilling companies, and after touring Terminal Sawmills facilities, company executives decided that it would fit nicely into Interfor's inventory. However, when they met with Asa over the following weeks, they decided that he wanted too much money, and they walked away from the negotiations.

CHAPTER SEVEN

The 1980s

In 1980, Asa appointed Darcy Johal superintendent of the umbrella company Terminal Forest Products. He was just thirty years old, but he had been working for his father since he was an eleven-year-old, cleaning up the mill on weekends and after school. Now he was responsible for everything from the hiring of crews to daily lumber production. Over the next ten years he would move up to the job of company president, advising the CFO, attending lumber conventions and building relationships with existing and new buyers from the United States.

However, those ten years would prove to be difficult for Terminal Forest Products—as well as for the entire West Coast lumber industry. The decade began with the first round of Canada's softwood lumber dispute with the United States. The US construction industry was at that time—and remains to this day—heavily dependent on Canadian lumber because its needs far outstrip the available domestic supply, but in 1982 the American lumber industry petitioned the US Department of Commerce to impose countervailing duties on softwood lumber imported from Canada. They charged that it was subsidized by the Canadian government, allowing Canadian suppliers to undercut the price of American lumber and giving them an unfair trading advantage. The charge was based on the fact that in Canada, most forests are located on federal or provincial land, and logging companies pay the government "stumpage fees" to harvest the trees. But while stumpage in Canada was originally set according to the number of trees cut—that is, by foot board measure (FBM) or Scribner Scale—by 1980 it was calculated on the cubic metres of timber cut. The Americans claimed these rates were set too low, thus amounting to subsidization. In the US, on the other hand, 70 per cent of forests are privately owned and the logging companies buy their timber at auction, so stumpage rates are set in the competitive marketplace. British Columbia and Quebec, the major Canadian exporters of softwood lumber to the US, were most affected by the US industry's charges, but fortunately after a year of disruption, the US Department of Commerce ruled that Canada's stumpage system was not countervailable, and for the next few years the dispute returned to simmering quietly in the background.

Changing market conditions were also a contributing factor to the BC forest industry's troubles during the 1980s. Since World War II sawmill operators on the BC coast had been slowly developing a market in Japan for kiln-dried white woods (hemlock, balsam and Douglas fir), but in 1983 and again in 1984, Japan was struck with major earthquakes—the magnitude 7.8 Nihonkai-Chubu earthquake in May 1983 and the magnitude 6.3 Otaki earthquake in September 1984. The scale of lives lost and the widespread collapse of buildings prompted the Japanese government to institute a complete overhaul of building codes in that country, especially for commercial buildings, and the new codes wiped out most of BC's white wood market there. For Asa it meant the loss of a budding export market for his kiln-dried hemlock.

The year of the Otaki earthquake also brought labour troubles at Asa's Mainland Sawmills, which had been running three shifts a day to keep up with the demand for custom-cut lumber. The troubles started out as a dispute over a single job promotion after a head sawyer's position had become available, and Asa, knowing none of his present employees were qualified to step into this very difficult job, hired a man from the outside. The workers, who were all members of the International Woodworkers of America, demanded that he give the job to one of their fellow long-term employees, even though the man in question wasn't qualified to do it, and at the same time they began demanding wage increases across the board. When Asa refused to concede, they staged a wildcat strike that brought the sawmill's production to a standstill. The next step was negotiations with the union, but Asa still refused to put a man into a job he didn't have the qualifications to do, even if he was a long-standing employee. Mainland's manager, Albert Kovlaske, explains, "It was important to Asa and me to only have qualified people working on the machines, and the workers weren't willing to give up the right to make those decisions." While the strike continued, they met again and again with union officials, but Asa wouldn't back down. Avtar remembers telling him, "You've got to give them something," but Asa would just say, "No, I'll leave it shut down forever."

Despite what Asa was saying, he knew he had to get production at Mainland going again because it was such an important element in Terminal's business, but what he really wanted to do was fire the men responsible for the wildcat strike. As a result, when the next union-management meeting was scheduled, Albert offered to step in on Asa's behalf. "I told them that Asa had something else on that day, so he couldn't come. So then these guys were jumping all over me saying, 'You got to do this,' and 'You got to do that,' and Doug, who was on the union executive, said, 'Just a minute, guys. Albert came here by himself, so let's be reasonable about what we're doing.' So we sat down and decided on the one guy we were going to fire for initiating the wildcat strike and the one guy we would suspend. The employees went back to work the next day." Mainland Sawmills eventually settled down, and in future Asa was allowed to hire someone from outside the company if a senior employee quit and there was no one qualified already on the payroll.

With the strike settled, Albert went back to trouble-shooting production problems. One of them involved the custom-cutting services at the Mainland plant. Customers were bringing high-value Douglas fir, western hemlock, spruce and cedar logs to be cut with Mainland's precision machinery, but unless the wood had been kiln-dried, the freshly cut lumber often developed mildew and fungus before it was shipped. Giving this lumber an anti-stain treatment eliminated the problem, but it meant extra handling. What the mill needed was an automatic system, and he designed one where, immediately after the logs were cut into lumber, each board passed through a chamber where it was sprayed with anti-stain solution. He also created a self-cleaning spray nozzle for this chamber and a set-up where the overspray was captured, filtered, recycled and stored safely in protected tanks to be ready for re-use. Later he installed the same system at Terminal Sawmills and Terminal Planer Mill.

Next, to break down the shavings at the planer mill so that more shavings could be fitted into a bunker or chip truck, Albert found a machine called a "fractionator" that would take the shavings from the planers and cut them into smaller pieces. "He had to make some modifications to it," Avtar recalls, "but it did produce an acceptable product." With this problem resolved, Albert then set about improving the suction systems for planer shavings at both Mitchell Island Forest Products and Terminal Sawmills, as western red cedar is extremely abrasive and it was constantly wearing out the system's steel pipes, especially the elbows. His solution was to replace all the heavy wear portions of the system with stainless steel; it was more expensive but lasted ten times longer.

Another of Albert's projects at Terminal was to design and build a lift to handle bundle booms. In the 1980s, while some logs still arrived at the mill in flat booms (a single layer of logs), approximately 80 per cent of logs arriving there were bundled together in booms weighing up to 100 tons.[4] To save time getting these logs out of the river and into the mill, Albert's new machine hoisted an entire bundle of logs out of the water at once and moved it into position hydraulically.

In 1983 Albert ordered a Debimatic Chop Saw from France for the Mitchell Island plant; it was designed to cut kiln-dried boards into shorter lengths and square off the ends. With this new system, each length was manually marked with a fluorescent crayon at the point where it was to be cut before being fed into a scanner; there a special camera and a tracking wheel encoder read the mark's position on the board, and that information travelled to the main computer. The board was then moved along via hydraulic servo valves until it was positioned for the cut. This system proved to be more than twice as fast as manually cutting the boards.

In June 1985 the softwood lumber dispute boiled over again after US producers, who were now organized as the Coalition for Fair Lumber Imports, lobbied Washington for redress through the International Trade Commission (ITC). At the same time they filed a countervail petition for an import duty of 27 per cent on Canadian lumber; unfortunately, BC Premier Vander Zalm chose this moment to announce that stumpage rates in BC actually were too low, in essence agreeing with the US complaints. In June 1986 the ITC ruled that imports of Canadian lumber were damaging the American industry, and later that year Ottawa agreed to impose a 15 per cent tax on all softwood lumber destined for the US market. For Terminal Forest Products this agreement meant that, though the company bought all its logs at open market prices rather than logging them and paying stumpage, it would now, like all Canadian softwood exporters, be taxed on the lumber it exported to the US. In late 1987 the federal government reached agreements with BC and Quebec whereby they would charge higher stumpage fees in exchange for Ottawa cancelling the 15 per cent tax. And there the dispute seemed to have been resolved.

In spite of the softwood lumber dispute, a wildcat strike and the loss of the Japanese hemlock market, Terminal Forest Products still made progress in the 1980s. The company was turning out higher quality products than the competition as well as innovating with several new product introductions. "We were grading the lumber higher than most companies," Avtar recalls, "and to a higher standard than government and Council of Forest Industries's grading books mandated. We provided special grades to suit our customers' needs and we cut the logs a certain way to get better-looking lumber. We gave them knots in their

A Mainland sawmill worker is busy grading and sorting incoming logs.

boards if they wanted them, and for others who didn't want knots, we customized for them but always with a higher standard."

One of those who noticed the high quality of Terminal's products was Barry Kaye, the general manager of the Long Island distribution centre of the American Lumber Company, an important distribution wholesaler of building materials in the eastern United States. In mid-1982 American Lumber had recruited Kaye (whose business degree was from Wharton and whose LL.D. was from NYU) from his successful independent consultancy to turn the performance of the company's struggling Long Island unit around. One day in the latter part of that year, Kaye's market-savvy young foreman, Richard Paci, sent word to the upstairs office, inviting Kaye to come to the railroad siding behind the company warehouse where stevedores were unloading a Thrall all-door boxcar, a freight car with four large sliding doors on each side that gave access to its entire length. This particular boxcar was loaded with patterned cedar panelling, and Kaye recalls that he "automatically feared that it might be an alarm about damaged incoming freight ... On the contrary, the cedar units had been skilfully packaged, protected and loaded, but what was most important was the first glimpse of the actual pieces of panelling pulled from their wrappings. What struck Richie (and me, of course) was the unprecedented perfection manifested in that finished product. Relative to any product, softwood or hardwood, that we had ever received, these cedar pieces actually had the look— and, to some extent, even the feel—of precision metal parts! I phoned my father, S.M. Kaye, [American Lumber's vice president] in our New York City office to ask how our company had come by this remarkable cedar product. He told me he had been to the Pine Show in San Francisco where he was introduced to 'a very nice chap' by the name of Glenn Connor, the manager of cedar sales for Vancouver-based Canfor." It was through Connor that Kaye had ordered the railcar of cedar panelling.

With his father's permission, Barry Kaye followed up by phoning Connor to explore the idea of American Lumber becoming a US distributor for this product, and that is when he learned that the manufacturer was Terminal Forest Products, for which Canfor was then the exclusive cedar sales agent. After investigating American Lumber and satisfying himself that the company would demonstrate the necessary dedication, Connor permitted Kaye to purchase, stock and distribute Terminal's cedar products. Kaye reports that, "it wasn't long before Glenn Connor phoned to confide that American Lumber had become the largest dollar-volume customer in the world for TFP's cedar products ... and so, he reckoned, it was 'time for us to meet the folks.'" It was shortly after this that the Kayes, father and son, set out on "a western mill trip," which included the Vancouver area, and they met the driving force behind Terminal Forest Products, Asa Johal. Barry Kaye quickly became one of Asa's admirers. "In all the years I have known him, never once have I heard him succumb to the temptation of braggadocio, even though by any standard he has had so much about which he quite legitimately might have boasted. Neither is Asa given to either pretense or the slightest facade. Rather, he may well be the most truthful and forthcoming man you ever will meet. My further impressions as the years have gone by include that his passion regarding his company, its production and its products has been at such a fevered level so consistently and for so long as to merit the characterization of a 'natural wonder.'"

It is interesting to note that by the time Barry Kaye purchased American Lumber in 1999, he had become the general manager of the entire company; his son Joshua Kaye, who has business and economics credentials from Dartmouth and Oxford, recently took over management and control. But in spite of all the changes and challenges that have arisen through the years, the foundations of loyalty between American Lumber and Terminal Forest Products have remained strong.

By 1985 roughly 90 per cent of Terminal's cedar products were being shipped to international distributors but the company was about to reach deeper into the US with a boost from Robert Ankner, CEO and president of Boston Cedar. Ankner recalls, "We met in 1982 or '83 when I was working for MacMillan Bloedel as a manager in Massachusetts, and I went into a meeting with Wells Wilkinson and Asa Johal in Boston. We discussed the possibility of buying cargo lumber [dimensional, construction-grade lumber used for framing homes], though that idea never panned out.

"Fast forward to a Friday morning in February 1985. Three of us managers—myself, Tony Morgan and Bob Vasquezi— decided to resign to start our own company—Boston Cedar. When we made that announcement, MacMillan Bloedel spread the word to the lumber industry that they wouldn't welcome anyone who supplied cedar to us ... they blackballed us. We arrived in Vancouver after being in business for only a week or two and went knocking on doors of one lumber office after another. We spent the entire week in Vancouver and covered almost every cedar producer ... and we were going back to Boston with no cedar supply to offer the American market. It looked like we were going to be the shortest company in history to go out of business. MacMillan Bloedel's dirty tactics had won.

"As we were about to leave for the Vancouver airport, I turned to Bobby and said, 'I remember meeting this guy shipping cedar products to Bernie Bernstein in the US ... We should go see him. What do we have to lose? We've been turned down by everyone.' We hopped into a taxi and headed to Mitchell Island to Terminal Forest Products ... We sat down with Wells Wilkinson and I put all my cards on the table. I told him everything, including the fact that my previous employer, MacMillan Bloedel, had blackballed us in this town. Wells marched us into Asa Johal's office, where we met Asa and his son-in-law, Avtar Opal, who managed Mitchell Island Forest Products. We repeated our story to them, and Asa turns to me and says, 'Someone tried to do that to me when I was first starting out. It was a horrible experience.' Asa, Avtar, Wells and I had a connection immediately, but I knew I had to ask the question, 'Would you supply us with your cedar products?' Asa was very business-like and he thought about it for about a second. 'Will you pay your bills on time?' he asked. I turned to Avtar and I said, 'I will discount every invoice.' [Invoices are discounted by 1 per cent if they are paid on time.] Avtar smiled and Asa said calmly, 'That's good enough for me.' Asa's company became our only supplier of western red cedar products. We bought as much of his finished manufactured cedar products as we could get and sold them to the housing market in America." At that time Boston Cedar had to buy Terminal's products through Canfor Industries, but after Canfor and Terminal Forest Products parted ways in 1997, Boston Cedar bought directly from Terminal, only going to other cedar suppliers if Terminal couldn't meet their demand.

"Over the next thirty years everybody and his boy came out of the woodworks in BC to sell cedar to us after they learned we had done hundreds of millions of dollars of business with Asa," Ankner said, then added, "Where are most of these corporate giants now? Almost all have failed, but Asa's Terminal Forest Products is still standing and thriving. It's a beautiful story, and Asa built a hell of a company." (In 2017, Ankner sold Boston Cedar to US Lumber, headquartered in Atlanta, Georgia.)

———

Although business was booming for Asa in the 1980s, he still had a constant battle to get enough logs for his mills. He needed to get into the logging business as well as milling so he wouldn't have to buy logs from Canfor and on the open market. A possible solution to this problem appeared in 1986 when his log buyer, Robbie Thurston, heard of a logging company in trouble. L&K Lumber had large timber holdings on the Sunshine Coast, just north of Vancouver, as well as holdings farther north in the Bute Inlet area, plus cutting rights on Crown land for a total of 350,000 cubic metres of mixed species, 15 per cent cedar and the rest fir and hemlock. L&K had started out in North Vancouver before moving to Langdale on Howe Sound, where they had built a sawmill and established a 35-acre (14.6-hectare) dryland log-sorting operation off Twin Creeks Road. Here their logs were sorted, graded and scaled before being sent to a central sorting ground or their final destination. But L&K had poor production levels, and they also had a serious problem disposing of their sorting ground waste.

When Asa, Albert and Avtar went to see the properties, the company had just passed into receivership. "Imagine a situation where the company owners at one time had $32 million," Asa says, "and after going through a series of problems going broke and *owing* $32 million." He purchased all of the company's assets, guaranteeing him a steady log supply. "I think I paid $15 million, and I made a deal to give them [L&K] part of my profits for five years, which I did. I also bought a tax loss from them at the time, and I used all that up."

The Langdale log-sorting operation had a number of issues that required Albert's urgent attention, but the most serious problem was how to deal with the mountains of mixed solid wood and bark debris that accumulated from the sorting process. They decided that the only possible way to dispose of it was to separate the wood from the chunks of bark, and Albert set about creating a reclaiming machine that tumbled the debris; the solid wood that came out one end of the drum was conveyed directly to a chipper and the resulting chips were then barged to Canfor's mill at Port Mellon to be turned into pulp. The bark that came out the other end travelled to a mulching machine to make hog fuel, which the pulp mill burned to produce steam. This reclaiming machine was no sooner in operation than Albert was threatened with a lawsuit for copyright infringement. Fortunately, he was able to produce his drawings to prove that he had designed it, and the other party backed down.

In 2000, Terminal Forest Products sold the L&K forest tenures to A&A Trading but continued to operate the Langdale sorting ground.

CHAPTER EIGHT

Family Affairs

In spite of the changes and tumult at Terminal Forest Products during the 1980s, Asa had begun taking more time to be with his wife, children and grandchildren. His granddaughter Razia Opal, Geven and Avtar's daughter, recalls going on holiday to the home Asa had bought in Palm Springs with "Grandma and *Baba Ji* [Asa] when I was seven years old in 1983 or '84. They took me and the other grand-kids—Roop and Sanjay—by ourselves. This was my first vacation away from home without my parents, and it was my first plane ride, and it's the place where I learned to swim. *Baba* was more relaxed there than he was in Vancouver. He wore shorts and enjoyed sitting outside in the sun watching us in the pool. While we swam, he would read several news-papers front to back."

While there, however, Asa received word that his mother was very ill. He had grown closer to her after his father died in 1964, making up for some of the quality time they had missed in the earlier years, but by 1983 Tej Kaur's health was deteriorating, and he had hired a live-in caretaker to attend to her physical needs and keep her company. She was now seventy-eight years old.

When Asa and Kashmir arrived back in Vancouver, they discovered that Tej Kaur had developed gangrene in her right foot and the infection was spreading up her leg. They took her to the hospital, where the emergency room doctor informed them that her situation had deteriorated to the point where they would need to amputate her leg above the knee. Family members had a torrent of questions, but Asa understood immediately that she needed the amputation to save her life, and as the eldest son he gave permission to have this done. After Tej Kaur returned home, Kashmir visited regularly to make sure her caregivers were soaking and dressing her wound properly and dealing with her other physical limitations. "We bought her one of these powered carts so she could get around," Asa recalls, "and she loved it." But after a time it became apparent to Asa and Kashmir that Tej Kaur needed more care than could be provided at home, and they arranged for her to be admitted into a senior citizens' home near them in Richmond. Tej Kaur died in 1985.

Although Asa was saddened when his mother died, he realized that during their lives his parents had been more concerned with finances than bonding with their children. "This is why I find it hard to express my feelings of love to my own family," he says. But his grandchildren certainly felt his love. According to granddaughter Roop Johal, Manjit and

Family is very important to Asa. Although he was a busy man, he tried to reserve time to spend with his children and grandchildren. He is pictured here with his entire family at his and his grandson Sanjay's birthday party.

Darcy's daughter, "It was never said out loud to Sanjay or me or Rummen, but you could feel the love by the small things *Baba* would do with us." And granddaughter Neera Opal, Geven and Avtar's daughter, agrees. "Even though he never verbally expressed his love for us, I feel the opportunities he gave us for a better life were his form of communicating that. He has always stood beside us financially and supported all of us ... I can confidently say I never would be in the position I am in my life without his work ethic. As a family, we have all thrived due to his tireless hours at the business and the sacrifices he made."

Everyone understood that his time was limited, but when he could spare a moment, he would gather his grandchildren and put them into his car and drive them up to the pharmacy to do errands. The grandchildren were excited because they knew the trip would entail buying candy. Asa, however, acknowledges that he has always relied on Kashmir to carry the family, as she had the radar to know when her children or grandchildren needed emotional or financial help. She was the go-to person for everyone in the extended Johal family. Razia Opal explains that "the family is together because of my Grandma Johal," and Roop Johal pointed out that because of her grandmother, "we were a tight family while we were young."

———————

By the mid-1980s Terminal Forest Products was making very good money, and in 1986 Asa took a bonus of $110 million after taxes, part of it being repayments from the softwood tariffs returned by the US to the Canadian forest industry. Over the years he had occasionally invested money elsewhere than in his company, but he says, "I didn't have much luck at that." He lost a few million dollars through one company and another $1.5 million through an investment broker. Only once did he have financial payback on a stock investment, and that was through an American named Bernie Bernstein who owned Mid-State Lumber, a wholesaler in New Jersey. Bernstein had been introduced to Asa by Jack McMillan of Canfor in

Kashmir is the heart and soul of the extended Johal family. Everyone in the family goes to her for help. Clockwise from top left: Manjit, Roop, Shyla, Kashmir, Debbie.

the late 1970s, and as the years went by he became one of Terminal's major distributors in the northeastern US, and eventually Asa's close friend. "He [Bernstein] got me to put $600,000 into US bank stocks," Asa recalls. "Then the banks turned over new owners twice, and I ended up with a million dollars. That's the only time I made money on the stocks." Asa quit investing in other commodities in the late 1980s.

While Asa was becoming successful, Kashmir had been quietly asking him for a bigger and newer house. It was important to her for the family to continue to live together in the traditional multi-generational manner, but the grandchildren were older now and the family needed more room. Asa, however, saw no need for a new house, especially the custom-built sprawling mansion with state-of-the-art technology Kashmir had in mind. She persisted, trying many times to explain why she wanted it, but he was plainly not interested. Then one day in 1987 she shared her frustration with her daughter, Geven, and Geven took on her father. "I discussed it with Dad and told him that his dream was the mill," says Geven, "but Mom's dream was having this new home. And he finally understood." Although Kashmir had expressed her wishes quite plainly, it was only when Geven became engaged in the conversation that she got her house. As Asa explains it, "Over the years Kashmir and I have gone to Geven when we need to work through problems. She can be impartial and see what would be best for the family."

After his discussion with Geven, Asa found a house on 54th Avenue in Kerrisdale. "The owner needed money. I think he was in trouble. So I offered him $1.3 million cash and he took it. My intention was to rip down the existing house and build a new one on the property, so we rented a townhouse at 57th and Granville for the next three years because it took that long to get the permits and build it. My wife hired an architect, the same man that Geven had used, Don Delinsky, and together with the builder, they designed our new home. Manjit and Darcy were involved somewhat, but it was mainly Kashmir's project."

Architect Don Delinsky was a multi-talented man and helped Kashmir with the design ideas as well as supporting her selection of interior furnishings. Both Asa and Kashmir wanted every inch of the house to be used but still ensure privacy for everyone living there. "Kashmir was particular about the furnishings," Asa explains, "including the rare cherry wood imported from Brazil that we used in the interior. It was important for her and Don to use the best products."

The dynamics of the family's traditional living arrangements were complex, and Roop explains that as they grew older, there were downsides for the grandchildren. "It was almost like living with two sets of parents, except that Grandpa never interfered with anything. I don't remember him saying anything. Living with them and coming home in the middle of the night, it wasn't just Mom you had to deal with—it was Grandma Kashmir standing at the window. And when you got in trouble, you didn't just get in trouble with Mom, you had to deal with the whole goddamn family. It was a family affair when something went wrong—like if you were dating a guy that nobody liked, it was a serious family affair. But my grandpa never, ever, ever said anything. My connection with him remained special. With my grandma, it's with my brother Sanjay. They have a relationship where they can fight, but they can't live without each other either. I have that with my grandpa Asa."

While Asa had experienced difficulty being close to his own children, he did make a much greater attempt to be a factor in his grandchildren's lives. If they had questions, they all knew he would give straightforward and honest answers.

His first grandson, Sanjay, appreciated that. "I remember being ten years old and asking my grandfather for money. He told me I would have to earn it, and he offered me a job at his lumber mill. At the time I didn't understand what he was trying to accomplish by giving me a job, but as an adult, I value the lessons he has taught me throughout my life about hard work and integrity. Through all the hardest moments in life, my grandfather has always been by my side and supported me unconditionally."

According to Manjit, her father-in-law sometimes bought things for his family even when they didn't want them. After she and Darcy took their children to visit farming friends near Kelowna, she found she missed the open agricultural lands of India. "When we came back from Kelowna, I said something to my mother-in-law and father-in-law about wanting to live on a farm. I only said it a couple of times in conversation, but I must have said it enough that my father-in-law heard me. Then he found this farm that was for sale in Richmond, and he took me to look at it. I remember it was $700,000 or $750,000. I thought that was too expensive—this was thirty years ago. I felt guilty about asking him for it because I wasn't used to asking for anything. Besides, it was going to be a hobby farm at best for me. I told him that it was too expensive, and I didn't need it. Three years later the price went down to $500,000, and the realtor phoned my father-in-law and said the same farm was still available. My father-in-law did not ask me. He just bought it for me without discussing it further. He showed up with the papers at home and told Darcy and me to sign them. He said, 'It's for your farm.' I said, 'Just like that?' He said, 'Just like that!' I asked him if it was in my and Darcy's name. He said, 'Yes.' All this because he heard me say I wanted a farm."

In the years that followed that purchase, Manjit and Darcy would spend several months at a time living in the farmhouse. She explains, "It was a fun place for the entire summer, for Easter and all the other statutory holidays. That gave Mom and Dad a break from us, and we got the experience of life on our own. We bought pets there and go-carts for the kids. Darcy built a skateboard ramp for the boys and a little house like a dollhouse for the kids to play in. We have used the farm as a home for the children, friends and guests. I also turned it into a spiritual retreat centre. We still have it, but now we rent it out."

Asa and Kashmir firmly believe that what they do for one of their children they must do for the other. It's all about striking a balance and keeping things equal between the siblings, so after buying a farm for Manjit and Darcy, naturally Asa felt he had to buy a farm for Geven and Avtar. "So he goes out and buys the adjacent farm for Avtar and me," Geven recalls. "But I say, 'I don't want to live on a farm!' He says, 'What? But I bought it for you.' I tell him I don't want it, and I want to move into Vancouver. I tell him, 'I'm driving my kids to private school from Richmond every day, and it's a long commute, and I don't want to live on a farm.' He bought it without asking me, and then he had to sell it when I refused to keep it." Eventually when Geven and Avtar found a home in Vancouver they liked, they sold their Richmond home, and Asa helped to finance the purchase of their new home.

While accepting the fact that the Johal family was busy and not that emotionally demonstrative, Geven and Avtar often turned to Avtar's aunt, Jeeto Oujla, and his aunt and uncle, Surjit and Jeet Uppal, and when the three Opal children, Razia, Neera and Rajeev, were young, their parents often relied on the Opals and Uppals and their families to help out with their babysitting needs. Gradually and quite naturally they developed a strong emotional bond with them, knowing they would receive love and affection there. That closeness has lasted throughout their lifetime.

Meanwhile, the bonds that had held Asa's family loosely together were breaking down. His sister Mary had been diagnosed in her early life as bipolar, and after living for many years with her parents, she spent the last fifteen years of her life in an assisted living home. At that time Asa and Kashmir had taken on the guardianship of her daughter Paula, bringing her into their home and raising her. Kashmir had been the only family member to visit Mary, always taking Paula with her, and Asa took care of Paula's wedding costs. When Mary died, they sold her house and gave the money to Paula so that she would be secure for her future.

There would be one more death in the family around that time: Joe, the youngest of Asa's siblings. As a young adult, he had worked for Asa at the sawmill, but he hadn't stayed for long. "Joe left home young," Asa says, remembering. "He got involved in drugs and alcohol, and they destroyed him." The police found Joe's badly beaten body in a rundown area near Hastings Street in January 1992, and Asa was called to the morgue to make the identification. He had never seen violent death so close to him and the corpse was just a mass of broken bones, blood and bruises. "My brother Joe and I didn't have a good relationship," Asa acknowledges, "but when he died, I felt sad. Often when he was sober, he would bring toys over for Darcy and Geven, and he was always kind to them. But when he was drunk, it was a different story."

It couldn't have been easy for Asa, recalls his friend and financial advisor, Anant Pal Singh. "Everybody has ups and downs in life, but the only time I saw Asa down was when he had to identify his brother Joe's body. He was very quiet. He didn't show anything, and he was just calm." No one was ever charged with Joe Johal's murder.

CHAPTER NINE

The 1990s

T he next round of the softwood lumber dispute began in 1991 with Canada withdrawing from the 1986 Memorandum of Understanding, and the US Department of Commerce (DOC) retaliating by immediately imposing countervailing duties. The picture had changed somewhat since the last round of the dispute, however, because the two countries had signed the Canada-US Free Trade Agreement (CUSFTA) in October 1987, and by its terms Canada now had the option of presenting its case to a bi-national panel. This panel—three Canadians and two Americans—found in favour of Canada; when the DOC challenged this decision, the dispute was brought before an "extraordinary challenge committee," where the wrangling went on for another five years.

As the conflict continued, Asa returned to his plan of manufacturing high-value cedar products intended for the US market in a facility in that country because the new US countervailing duties on rough lumber were much lower than on finished products. According to Asa, "I always wanted to be in the finished wood products business in the US since over 90 per cent of my lumber products were sold in the US by that time. I knew it would cut down on my transportation costs, so it made good sense to be in the business on that side of the border." His decision was also influenced by the lower labour costs in the US. However, by this time he had sold the property in Ferndale, Washington, and was forced to begin the search for another location close to his Vancouver base but convenient for his American customers.

His attention turned to Everson, Washington, where the Jones family had run into financial troubles with their independent remanufacturing plant, the South Everson Lumber Company (SELCO). The plant was known principally for producing fence boards, although the family had also been custom cutting and upgrading lumber for their customers. Unfortunately, both the SELCO building and its equipment were old and dilapidated, and the family could not afford to repair the roof, which had collapsed during a heavy snowfall the previous winter. When Asa learned they were looking to sell, he offered them $1.5 million US and they were happy to take it. What he saw in that rundown plant was immense opportunity. Over the next year he sank more than $15 million US into SELCO, tearing down the old plant and building a new one, installing new equipment, paving the 40-acre (16.2-hectare) site and fencing the yard. He then appointed Avtar president of the new US facility.

The SELCO plant was located in the US and primarily responsible for fence boards. However, the plant did custom cutting and upgrading lumber as well.

Despite now owning the US remanufacturing plant he had wanted for so long, Asa had every intention of keeping Mitchell Island Forest Products, his Canadian remanufacturing plant, operating, but labour troubles developed there in 1993. The company was running two shifts but having issues with workers needing time off, which meant the plant was often operating short-handed. This problem was complicated by the fact that the IWA had been trying to unionize the workers for a long time, and although most of them were already getting union wages, benefits and a pension plan, they were eager to join the union. Avtar had told them that if they couldn't work things out without the union, the company would probably have to shut down specific pieces of equipment or whole production lines because of the increased cost. "I told them the efficiency of the operation would determine whether their jobs would be there or not. I said, 'We are up against the competition, and we can't afford to pay union wages for those people on finger jointers because other outfits are paying half the wages and no benefits for doing that job.' I said, 'We are giving you benefits, but we can't pay you the same hourly wage.' But they wanted to make the same money as the union guys, and we couldn't make those products if we paid those wages because it was such labour-intensive work."

However, after operating for thirteen years without a union, in 1993 Mitchell Island Forest Products got certified and became unionized. With the higher labour costs that followed, it made financial sense for Asa to ship the machinery for the chop line, finger jointers and edge gluers from Mitchell Island to the new SELCO plant to take advantage of the lower costs. Eventually Asa moved most of the company's finishing work there from Vancouver, and Mitchell Island Forest Products was reduced to one line and one shift, which required a total of just nineteen employees to sort and grade the cedar lumber that was custom cut at Mainland and Terminal Sawmills. The sorted lumber was then sent to Terminal to be loaded into the dry kilns, and both Terminal and Mainland supplied this kiln-dried cedar to SELCO.

―――――――――

Gradually over the years the logs coming into Terminal's mills from the forest had become poorer in quality with more knots and defects, but for the company's bottom line it was very important that this less-than-perfect timber plus all the short pieces unsuitable for traditional products didn't go to waste. Like others in the industry faced with this problem, Asa had turned to finger jointing and edge gluing to utilize this wood. A finger jointer cuts "fingers" into both ends of wood that is too short to use for regular dimension lumber. These short pieces are then joined lengthwise— interlocking in the way that fingers of a person's hands can interlock—and glued to create longer pieces that are then trimmed to specific lengths. Each finger-jointed piece is then put through a ripsaw to make the edges perfectly parallel. Edge gluing involves taking multiple narrow widths of finger-jointed stock and gluing them together side by side to create wider pieces. At SELCO these pieces, which could be as wide as 36 inches (91 cm), up to 20 feet (6 m) long and 3 inches (7.6 cm) thick, were then custom-ripped into multiple sizes according to the purchaser's needs.

Finger jointing involves cutting "fingers" at the edge of a piece of wood and then gluing the fingers together to create one long piece of wood. This is done frequently in the industry to reduce waste.

"Most of our edge gluers at that time used radio frequency to cure the glue lines," Avtar explains. "It was a good system, except that if the moisture content in the wood was too high, the glue wouldn't bond—and that was a big problem. Asa told me numerous times about the very first time Terminal sent some wood away to a custom edge gluer, and this outside contractor put it through a radio-frequency drying machine. Our customer used the wood on the exterior of a home in Florida, but it soon began delaminating—that is, falling apart. The client was forced to remove it all and replace it with another product, which was obviously a big job. This created the considerable claim of $100,000 for us. Because of this, I didn't want to go with a radio frequency drying system, so we chose a process where we clamped the boards in place in a heated room for two hours so they could properly cure. We had to special order clamp carriers that were 20 feet [6 m] long, and as the room housing this equipment had to be temperature controlled, we had to install special heaters and fans. But it worked really well. We started with one machine and, when demand increased, we ordered a second one and installed it beside the first."

The challenge in the new SELCO plant was efficiency, which meant maximizing output with the least amount of waste or by-product, and this required a myriad of adjustments until they got it right. One of the early problems occurred when they were feeding the finger-jointed boards through the new planer moulder, a finishing machine that put a pattern on the surface of the rough finger-jointed boards. Some of the finished boards were coming out with chipped surfaces at the finger-joint line and had to be downgraded. After investigating, Avtar realized that changing the feed direction resulted in a vastly improved product, and he implemented a system of tracking the joint lines. "For example," he explains, "some of the finger-joint boards were produced by re-sawing a 2×6 into two pieces of 1×6, so all the 2×6 boards would need to be fed into the re-saw in a specific orientation based on the uniformity of the surface. The output of the re-saw would yield a top board and a bottom board, and these would have to be stacked in separate packages. They would then have to be fed into the moulder in a specific direction."

In 1995, Albert Kovlaske began working with Newnes Machinery of Salmon Arm to develop a prototype X-ray scanner for lumber, the first of its kind in the industry and a real game changer. Up to this time, knots and flaws in kiln-dried lumber had been marked by hand so they could be cut out by the chop saws, then the cut blocks would be finger-jointed and glued back together. This was a slow, labour-intensive process, but since knots and other defects have a higher density than the clear portions of a board, the new scanner they devised used an X-ray machine to locate these high-density areas then input their locations into a computer algorithm. The second part of the scanner took video snapshots of the board before casting a light shadow across it to locate its other characteristics. All this data was sent to an optimizer computer to get a unique cut solution for each board. The main computer then transmitted the cut list to two high-speed chop saws, and the cut blocks would be fed directly into the finger jointer. The waste was kicked out into chipper conveyors, while usable pieces went to a special ripsaw in-feed that carried them into another saw and a moulder that finger jointed the smaller pieces into blocks.

Initially the computer system on this new Newnes Scanner wasn't fast enough for the volume of data generated by the scan of each board, so the board had to be held back to wait for the computer to send the cut list to the chop saws.

Avtar recalls Asa coming very close to giving up on it. "Many times I had to convince him that we had to keep trying until we got it right. He would say, 'Forget it! This machine isn't working. We should just get our money back!' But I knew we were close—we just weren't there yet. But after about a year we were at 90 per cent efficiency, which I thought was pretty good. That machine could process 700 feet [213 m] of lumber a minute. The boards would get automatically scanned and then fed into the two chop saws, so it saved a lot of time." Barry Kaye of American Lumber admired Avtar's determination and persistence. "He held nothing back when it came to matters of production and quality assurance. He really set the pace in the early days of finger jointing, and his extraordinary coordination between SELCO and the Canadian side of Terminal's business was a crucial key to optimizing the company's total effectiveness."

Around 1997, Terminal Forest Products's long-standing relationship with Canfor came to an abrupt end. One of the reasons for this was Canfor's inability to provide Terminal with enough logs, but there was also a problem with the man Asa had to deal with at Canfor. "He was always complaining that our chips weren't any good," Asa recalls. "So I went to Mike Thompson of Catalyst Pulp and Paper, which operated several pulp mills in BC. I phoned him up and said, 'Let's have lunch.' Over lunch I said, 'I want this many logs in exchange for providing you with my chips.' And he said, 'Okay, it's a deal.' So I phoned the fellow up at Canfor that we couldn't get along with, and we had lunch. I said, 'If my products aren't any good, then let's part company.'" Canfor's management valued their deal with Terminal, and they went after the man who had been complaining about the chips and had caused Asa to turn to Catalyst. They made a concerted effort to patch things up, but it was too late. Asa had already given his word to Mike Thompson and he stuck to it. Terminal Forest Products is still with Catalyst today.

By now Asa was making 450 types of superior cedar products and offering distinctive services to his customers, but he was an independent sawmill owner and producer competing against the giant public companies in the cedar log market, and that was never easy. One of those public companies, MacMillan Bloedel, controlled at least 40 per cent of the cedar market in BC, and Interfor—after its purchase of Weldwood in 1995—controlled 30 per cent. Asa controlled just 15 per cent. "In the early part of my career as an independent," he recalls, "I found it very difficult to obtain logs for my operations because I didn't have my own forest tenures, and the big corporations made it extremely difficult for me." But by the mid-1990s he had become known as a lower-cost operator and his competitors envied his success.

About this time a rumour circulated in the industry that Asa might want out of the business, and they came knocking on his door. But it became apparent as soon as they approached him with an offer that he was not interested in selling.

CHAPTER TEN

Darcy's Mill

Darcy Johal had spent most of his life working at his father's company in various capacities, but by the mid-1990s he was ready to go out on his own. An opportunity presented itself in 1996 when he went to Siberia to attend a forestry conference and he was introduced to a group of men involved in forestry and wood processing in Lithuania, a country with large state-owned forests. Furniture-making by Scandinavian companies such as IKEA had gradually created a demand for this lumber, and by the time Darcy became interested, furniture-making and other wood-processing industries were providing more than 30 per cent of all the jobs in the country's manufacturing sector.

Now forty-six years old, he was more than ready for the challenge of starting his own company, and Lithuania looked like the perfect place to do it. On a subsequent visit to that country he found an old, rundown sawmill in the city of Vilnius and another small mill and furniture factory in the port of Klaipeda that could be converted. His idea was to deal primarily in spruce and pine, the most common species in Lithuania, and sell the lumber into the markets of North America. It was exactly the kind of project where he could test-drive his management skills, but he needed his father's financial help to get started. Asa discussed Darcy's plans with his investment advisor and friend, Anant Pal, who explains that he would "periodically give Asa my two cents' worth. Mr. Johal either accepts it or not—that's up to him. He asked my opinion when Darcy was doing his stuff in Lithuania, and I told him that if I were in his shoes, I would give him the help he was asking for. But as a business decision, I didn't think it a good one." But after mulling it over, Asa agreed to buy his son the two mills and the factory.

As Darcy closed in on the deal, the one person whom he neglected to consult was Manjit, and by the time he got around to telling her, the damage was done. "Darcy didn't seek my approval for the new business," she says, "nor did he talk it over with me to see if I was fine with his plan. He decided he was going and that was that. I was resentful at first. Every time he would depart or arrive from Lithuania, we would have a nasty quarrel, and Darcy would stand there and take my anger." The reality in the Johal household was that over the next twelve years Manjit was without a husband and the children were without a father for extended periods of time. "It was a challenge dealing with our kids, especially during their teenage years," Manjit says. "Plus I experienced pressure from the outside community because there was a rumour that Darcy had left the kids and me. But I did what I had to do. At times it was stressful, but I had no choice but to manage it."

During Darcy's long absences Asa became the primary male influence in the children's lives, and grandson Rummen reflects that, "one of the great things about *Baba Ji* is that he has no hidden agendas or secrets. He is always transparent." Rummen remembers that when he wanted some of his own money, his grandfather would employ him for a period, just as he had his older brother, Sanjay. "I remember at ten years old working for my *Baba Ji* to make money, and I learned tremendous respect for his work ethic. He is a great role model for me. He is extremely grounded." Then with a smile, Rummen adds, "And as a child he let me ride his golf cart around the sawmill."

According to Manjit, living with Asa and Kashmir taught the children good manners, respect for their elders, honesty, integrity and the value of hard work. "To my kids, Asa is the most valuable person in the whole family and not just because he is supporting them financially. They see how much he does for them in every other way ... Even the great-grandchildren, when they come to visit, they will go to him first. He loves to play the grandfatherly and great-grandfatherly role."

While this was going on at home, Darcy had been negotiating business contracts and hiring a workforce in Lithuania. He built a strong management team at his two new sawmills, where he soon had five hundred employees depending on him. Over the ensuing years his hard work and dedication paid off. "I grew my company from about $200,000 or $300,000 in sales up to $50 million. I grew it like crazy and got an award from the president of Lithuania three times for being the biggest exporter in the country. I was a big wheel there for the first ten years." At the same time he was often frustrated by the challenges of doing business there.

Asa and Anant Pal made "two or three trips over the first few years" to see how Darcy was doing, and Anant recalls that after their last visit, "my gut reaction was that this was going to be an uphill climb for Darcy over there. I looked at everything and said to myself, 'I don't think this is going to work.'" After that visit Asa also realized that his son was lonely, and he reported back to his daughter-in-law that Darcy needed her beside him and urged her to make a short-term move to Lithuania.

When Manjit arrived in Vilnius, she was surprised to find Darcy living in a modest two-bedroom apartment, doing his own laundry, washing his dishes and—shockingly—cooking his own meals. "Living on his own, my husband had become unspoiled. And he had become very frugal. He wouldn't allow me to spend lavishly on groceries. For the first time in his life he was counting his money and saving it."

Shortly after Manjit's arrival, she asked to see this company that Darcy had given up everything at home for. "I went to see the mill. The Lithuanian workers were full of sadness because it was a country full of oppression and depression. Darcy's employees thanked me profusely for allowing him to start his business there. They said to me, 'He's a godsend, a gift from God,' because for the first time in their lives they could put food on their tables." Manjit decided at that moment that Darcy's mission was to take care of these poor people in Lithuania, and her anger at her husband began to dissipate. However, she was now pulled in two directions because her teen-aged children were more than Kashmir and Asa could handle, and she realized it was best for all the family if she returned to Canada.

The one thing that Darcy had not understood was the level of corruption in the local government, and after twelve years in Lithuania, his business venture started to fall apart. "For one thing, there was tax fraud," he recalls. "The private business truckers that I was purchasing the logs from were buying logs from the government foresters. I would pay them for the logs and the VAT [value added tax] that was owed, but these truckers weren't paying the VAT to the government foresters." So one day, representatives of the Lithuania government came knocking on Darcy's door to slap him with an order for payment of tax he had already paid. "The government said I owed them something like nine or ten million dollars." But from his previous business experience, this didn't seem like such a big deal—he would simply explain what had happened and prove that he paid the VAT, and the situation would be resolved. "Then I found out that the middle guys who I was paying all the VAT to were partners with the tax man at the top, and because I refused to pay the tax a second time, they stopped my log supply. So that's how it all went bust. There was no way I was going to get anything resolved in a country like that. Not as a foreigner."

As Darcy tried to press on, more problems arose. One was the result of the difference in the work ethic between Canada and Lithuania. "When the workforce took a break," Asa explains, "they would halt all production, lock the doors and sit down to eat." But a much bigger problem than a workforce that wasn't too interested in working was the country's unstable currency. The foreign exchange market was on a roller-coaster ride at this time, and according to Asa, "One US dollar was worth five Lithuanian dollars, but then Lithuania joined the European Common Market, and there were even fewer euros to the US dollar," and Darcy couldn't make that work because he was selling into the US market. "Another factor that caused the company to fail was that he tried to expand the business too fast. He was always expanding it." Anant Pal, who could see what was happening, predicted its outcome: "At the end, of course, we all knew that it wasn't working out, and Mr. Johal had to step in to help." The family decided it was time for Darcy to return to Canada. "Well," Asa says, "if it's not going to be profitable, he might as well come home ... I gave him 50 per cent of the profits of the Lithuanian operation before the markets fell apart. And there used to be a duty on the lumber, and I gave it all back to him, $15 million that year." Asa absorbed a $35 million loss on the venture.

Anant Pal, as one of the people closest to Asa, knew that he was very proud of Darcy, but Darcy was discouraged and knew it was important that he discuss what had happened in Lithuania with his father. "I told my dad the whole thing. I felt I failed him, even though he was pretty gracious about it all." Asa, who had experienced his own share of false starts and failures in his early years, just said, "It happens."

CHAPTER ELEVEN

The 2000s

I n 1996 the US and Canada had signed a five-year trade accord known as the Softwood Lumber Agreement (SLA), limiting Canadian lumber exports to the US to 14.7 billion board feet per year. Three days after the SLA expired in April 2001, the US lumber industry once again petitioned the Department of Commerce to impose countervailing duties on Canadian softwood lumber. Then for the first time in the history of this dispute, the industry also asked for anti-dumping tariffs, claiming that Canadian suppliers were dumping their lumber on the US market at unfair prices, which were made possible by Canada's low stumpage rates. On April 25, 2002, the DOC announced that Canadian lumber would now be charged a total of 27.22 per cent in duties, and by February 2003 some fifteen thousand workers in the Canadian forest industry had been laid off, most of them in BC.

The World Trade Organization, various panels sponsored by the North American Free Trade Agreement (NAFTA), which had been signed in 1994, and the United States International Trade Commission proceeded to rule and counter-rule on the dispute, but it was not until July 2006 that a tentative new deal was reached. By its terms, Canada would be reimbursed $4 billion of the $5.3 billion its lumber exporters had paid to the us in duties since the expiration of the last agreement, and no further penalties would be levied. Canada's House of Commons passed the bill in September 2006 and it was signed into law on September 12; it was set to expire in October 2015.

Meanwhile, Terminal Forest Products was also experiencing problems. In 2004 the bc government through TransLink—Metro Vancouver's transportation network—had served notice that it intended to expropriate part of the company's Mitchell Island Forest Products site on Ash Street in order to build a bridge over the Fraser River to carry the new Canada Line to Richmond and the Vancouver International Airport. The Ash Street plant was a vital link in Asa's very successful chain of production, but since TransLink only wanted a portion of the property, he began making plans to adjust to the loss. Later, however, TransLink informed him that they had misjudged how much land would be needed for the bridge, and they would be expropriating the entire site. Naturally Asa was outraged because housing starts in the us were now at an all-time high and a disruption of this magnitude would cut his market share. He had no alternative, except to find a new site and build a new facility. He and Avtar looked at many properties, and in the end they chose a 5-acre (2-hectare) parcel of land belonging to Sawarne Lumber right next to Terminal Sawmills on Mitchell Island. According to Avtar, they chose it because of its convenience. "It's much better if your operation is all on one site so you're not trucking wood all over the place. Otherwise, you're facing massive transportation costs."

The next two years were hectic for Terminal. The Mitchell Island plant remained operational during the transition, turning out finished cedar products, though in order to prevent production shutdown losses, they added some new equipment to the Ash Street plant while keeping some of the original equipment, all of which would later be relocated to the new site. The new facility needed an innovative design and structure to meet their special requirements, and Albert Kovlaske worked tirelessly with Avtar and a team of specialists to get the 115,000-square-foot plant designed and built. However, there were many delays and setbacks, starting with the need for environmental testing of the site to make sure it wasn't contaminated. Construction was stalled again by the laborious Vancouver city building permit process and only saved when TransLink stepped in to get the project put to the top of the approvals list. Then it turned out the Sawarne property was not large enough to accommodate the new facility and they had to use part of the adjacent Terminal Sawmills property.

It took Asa, Albert, Avtar and their team two years to finish the new facility and relocate the remanufacturing equipment from Mitchell Island Forest Products on

Ash Street to the new site, where they also added an end stacker and a re-saw band mill. But now Asa felt their existing Newnes scanner, which produced blocks for finger jointing, was no longer efficient enough for their needs, and in 2006 he asked Albert and Avtar to search for a better machine. Fortunately, Avtar had heard of a new Lux scanning system out of Belgium that was having good results on other species of lumber in the US. "We weren't sure if it would be able to scan western red cedar lumber, so we sent three packs of our chop grade cedar to their nearest location, which was in North Carolina, where they were already using it on white woods. The Belgian builder calibrated the scanners on the Lux machine to locate all the defects as per our requirements, and after they did the test runs on our lumber, they invited us to go and watch the scanner in action. We went and watched and were very encouraged by the results." The system used both cameras and X-ray equipment, and the cameras were so good that even the concentric circular grain lines in the knots were visible in the scanned images. The combination of the image data and X-ray data was programmed to represent the location and size of all the knots on the board, and the information was then sent to the optimizer computer. Avtar explains, "We thought it would do the job, and we purchased it along with their system for handling the material behind it because it was better than what we had designed on our own. The new scanner could operate continuously, and the boards would drop and be swept to alternate sides to feed two super high-speed chop saws. There was no stopping, and our production increased dramatically. The new computers were so much faster than our old one, though we noticed that under certain conditions there was a problem, so the machine supplier installed even faster computers on the scanner to deal with this issue. Ultimately the complete new system was so fast that we buried our finger jointer with the volume of finger-joint blocks it turned out. It did an excellent job."

The new plant was in full operation by the end of 2007, just in time for the massive economic collapse of 2008 and the subsequent North American recession. The lumber market dried up, and Terminal had to weather the sudden and drastic drop in business. Unfortunately, Asa was sitting on a huge stockpile of logs and lumber, he had just spent millions and millions of dollars building the new plant, and now he didn't have enough work for it. It was a painful turn of events, but since Terminal Forest Products had been in good shape leading up to the crash, and since Asa had a good relationship with the banks, he was able to keep the company afloat.

The lack of demand continued into 2009, when the number of private housing starts hit its lowest level in fifty years. The entire BC forest industry suffered a major hit, and Asa took a $35 million loss. The depressing impact of the recession on BC's lumber production was softened only slightly by increased lumber exports to China.

But Terminal also had another problem at this time: TransLink had reneged on reimbursing the company for the expropriation of the Ash Street property as per the original deal, claiming that Asa had spent too much money building the new facility and fitting it with unnecessarily expensive equipment. When negotiations failed, it became apparent that Terminal Forest Products would have to sue TransLink. As Avtar had been running Mitchell Island Forest Products, Asa had given him the job of dealing with the expropriation, and now he left him to deal with the impending court case. According to Avtar, he didn't need the headache of taking on the monumental task of suing TransLink, but he couldn't bear the thought of his eighty-seven-year-old father-in-law having to go through all the details of the case on his own. The process dragged on for a year and a half as Avtar "went through every invoice to double check every charge to see whether it was relevant, and after a review of the guidelines for what was allowable and what wasn't, we adjusted our claim." The trial was set for the fall of 2009, but on the opening day TransLink asked for a delay in the court proceedings so they could discuss the case directly with Terminal Forest Products Ltd. to see if they could reach a settlement. They did, and as a result, TransLink was able to avoid court costs and prevent the final settlement price from becoming public knowledge.

By 2013 lumber markets had improved, and that year Canada exported more than $7.4 billion worth of lumber to the United States—the highest amount since 2006, when the two countries had agreed on a nine-year truce. Also, due in part to the opening of markets in China for both logs and lumber, logging in BC increased to its highest level in six years.

In the late 1990s, Asa had begun thinking about his successor as head of Terminal Forest Products but then delayed his decision when Darcy set up his own company in Lithuania. Although Darcy had returned to the company in 2008, in the intervening years there had been other changes. Throughout the construction of the new remanufacturing plant, Albert Kovlaske had been tasked with hiring all the engineers and contractors, but once the new plant was up and running, he resigned from Terminal. In all good business relationships, there is always a time for a parting of the ways. And there was another parting of the ways in 2011 when Avtar retired from the business.

However, in 2013 when Asa celebrated his ninety-first birthday, he realized that he should not delay naming his successor any longer. His decision on this matter had always been complicated by the fact that Terminal was a husband-and wife-owned business and therefore involved family estate planning. A second problem had arisen because Asa and Kashmir's daughter, Geven, had owned 45 per cent of Terminal Forest Products' "B" shares, while Darcy owned the other 55 per cent, so that both had a considerable financial stake in the business. (Asa owned all the A shares.) Like her brother, Geven had worked for her father's company earlier in her life and had then continued on a part-time basis as his public relations liaison. Often she would be called in to advocate on her father's behalf, articulating his ideas and visions

Avtar retired in 2011 after working for Asa for thirty years. Avtar played a
key role as an engineer for Terminal Forest Products before becoming the
manager of the Mitchell Island Forest Products operation.

when he couldn't communicate them himself to a broader audience. As a result, she had remained thoroughly familiar with the family business.

However, the idea of Geven and Darcy running the company together was impractical, as they had not grown up close and had not become close in adulthood. They were also very different in personality, and Geven wanted to pursue other endeavours. As a result, in 2001 she asked her father to buy out her shares so that her brother could inherit the family business. Asa met with his advisors and lawyers for their legal input and decided to honour his daughter's wishes. He says, "It was her choice. I didn't force her out. She didn't want to argue with her brother." Asa's financial advisor, Anant Pal, is convinced it was a smart move. "In hindsight, I think it was a wise decision to let one person have it rather than having sibling conflicts. You see so many families where there are conflicts and all kinds of bad blood running throughout the whole family over inheritances." As for Geven, she was happy to start her own business—a successful company called Ocorp Development Ltd.—that builds new homes, condominiums and townhouses in Kelowna, and she hired her son-in-law, Sam Sandhu, to help run it. Darcy Johal officially took over the reins at Terminal Forest Products in October 2016.

According to Albert Kovlaske, "From the bank's perspective, it was important to know who was going to carry the torch of the business once the original owner retired." Asa has concerns about the future because he believes the softwood lumber disputes with the United States will continue and hopes Darcy will be able to endure them. "I hope he's going to do well," he says, "though it's a tough business. My expectations are that Terminal Forest Products will survive for at least another generation, but I can't see it for the future generations. I don't think beyond Darcy there is anyone in the family who is interested in it." Darcy, however, is very happy in his new role. "It's like riding a bicycle when you've been doing it your whole life," he says. "There's no pressure when you are running a company if you know what you're doing."

The empire Darcy took over had grown from one small sawmill employing nine people back in 1960 to two large sawmills, a planer mill, a remanufacturing plant and a dryland log sorting and chipping facility that together employ more than five hundred people. And when Asa retired in 2016 the company was producing approximately 100 million board feet of value-added western red cedar lumber annually in more than 450 finishing products.

Today the company's Langdale log sorting facility is a modern, efficient operation covering 35 acres (14.2 hectares) of land fronting Howe Sound on BC's Sunshine Coast. Logs arrive by barge or bundled boom to be de-watered by a bundle side lift and spread out on site where a team of graders inspect and mark each log for bucking to maximize value and prime lengths. Once scaled, the logs are sorted and re-bundled for shipment to customers' manufacturing facilities.

Asa (right) named Darcy (left) his successor in 2001. Darcy officially took over the company in 2016.

Logs arrive at the Terminal Sawmill on Mitchell Island by water and are cut into rough, green lumber that is sorted according to size and grade in preparation for further manufacturing. At the adjacent Terminal Planer Mill, the lumber is blanked, trimmed, re-graded and sorted to length. Most production then moves along to the nine gas-fired kilns to dry, and from there onto trucks to be transported across the border to the SELCO manufacturing plant. The waste wood is sent to various pulp mills.

Since Darcy has taken over the reins of the company, he has made it a priority to keep up with all the latest trends in technology, researching what other mills are using successfully. He has installed a new double arbor saw, a new step feeder, a board feeder at the J-bar and a merchandiser for processing the logs to length, as well as adding a saw filing room that allows for better and more accurate saw maintenance. Mike Woodland, manager of Terminal Forest Products, notes, "Darcy is working to get the best lumber recovery possible from the new installations." He has also been hiring a crop of young, smart and savvy people who can develop their skills within the company rather than hiring experienced people from outside who have worked for multiple companies. As the company now has long-standing relationships with buyers in the US, his primary market will continue to be south of the border. He has no plans to expand globally because there are already enough sales within the companies. He plans to stick with cedar as well.

CHAPTER TWELVE

Philanthropy

During the years that Asa Johal was off making the next big deal for Terminal Forest Products, his wife, Kashmir, was making weekly visits to the *gurdwara* and quietly introducing the spiritual practices of the Sikh faith to her husband and children. An integral part of that faith, she taught them, is the practice of *seva*, which means providing a service to the Sikh community and to others. This service can come in many forms: spending time helping others, studying and teaching the holy scriptures, donating money to charities or helping people in need. According to Darcy, "My mom was the first one to give to the church and family. My dad was not into religion in a big way. He's into the culture, but religion was a little different. When my mom started giving back, my father realized there's nothing wrong with giving to good causes and to extended family members. It makes him feel good, and it's the right thing to do."

Darcy's sister, Geven, had already become active in fundraising for York House and St. George's, two schools her children attended, and she encouraged her father to give to charity. "If someone came to my dad and asked him for a donation, he always gave. I don't know that he ever said no. Even if he couldn't give what they asked him for, he would give them something." But Anant Pal, who has seen the philanthropy of many business leaders in North America, says that Asa's giving is different in that he puts his spiritual practices into action out of love. "He has that kind of special heart that wants to help people and organizations. Some people have more money, but they don't have his heart."

Most of Asa's giving in his early years concerned the Sikh community in Vancouver, but beginning in the early 1970s as Vancouver and the Lower Mainland experienced a new wave of South Asian immigration, some of his giving involved him in conflict. Even though these new people spoke the same language, had the same skin colour, ate similar cuisine and shared a history from the Punjab, they practised a far more fundamental Sikhism, and as they took seats on *gurdwara* boards, they began implementing more conservative religious practices. Many of the pioneer Sikhs found it difficult to watch their *gurdwaras* being taken over. Balbir Jawanda, who twice served as president of the India Cultural Centre of Canada, explains that the newcomers "wanted to see Vancouver's Ross Street *gurdwara* run like *gurdwaras* were run back in India, and they began to demand change. Our pioneers and their children rejected some of their strict traditional practices, like covering their heads, eating meals on the floor and removing chairs and benches from the kitchen area."

Over the next decade distrust increased between the two groups, leading to less cooperation between the old community and the new, and a small group of pioneer men began gathering privately to discuss the problem. Finally it was agreed that the answer was the establishment of a community centre. What they had more difficulty agreeing on was what this centre's social parameters would be. Would it be a place for both men and women to gather? Would it be a place of worship? After all, some of the people in the group had by now been kicked out of the Ross Street *gurdwara* and no longer had a place to worship. Or was it to be just a place to hold parties? Would they serve alcohol or tea?

By June 1983 six Sikh business leaders had been persuaded to donate $5,000 each in exchange for membership shares in a new India Cultural Centre of Canada; their ultimate goal was to raise $1 million and form a charitable society. Asa Johal would provide $100,000, which would go toward purchasing the 10-acre (4-hectare) parcel of farmland with a house and barn on it that they had discovered for sale on Number 5 Road in Richmond. The group borrowed another $450,000 from the State Bank of India and closed the deal to purchase the property on June 30, 1983; since an official name for the project had not yet been chosen, five of the donors would act as trustees and sign the deed to the land as individuals.

Around that time, Asa decided to make a personal will, and his lawyers insisted that the property on Number 5 Road had to be listed as one of his assets since his name was on the deed, but he was equally insistent that it was communal property. When he reported back to the group, they expressed their dissatisfaction with making the property a communal asset, and Asa then suggested that they remove the names of the trustees from the deed and substitute the new name for their project: the India Cultural Centre of Canada. Some of the trustees were not present at this meeting, however, and when they objected to the name that had been selected and requested their money back, Asa personally offered to buy each of their $5,000 membership shares for $10,000. All agreed. But the day he was to pay them, some demanded another $7,000 for a total of $17,000. Asa refused.

As the majority of the trustees were satisfied with the new name, it was officially registered at the New Westminster Land Title Office, but three weeks later three of the disgruntled trustees hired a lawyer to contest both the transfer of the land and the project's name change. By now it was late 1984, and the then mayor of Richmond, Bill Blair, and a journalist from a Richmond newspaper had got wind of the troubled situation and were about to take the story public. The mayor wasn't enthusiastic about having a *gurdwara* in his backyard, and the city was concerned that the group hadn't adhered to the bylaws regarding properties in the Agricultural Land Reserve. This was the first that the cultural centre's trustees had been aware that they needed a special permit to build on land within the ALR, but they hired legal assistance and eventually got the necessary permit. As for the newspaper's exposé, the trustees turned to Jack Uppal, another sawmill owner, to approach the journalist—who was a good friend—and Uppal talked him out of writing the piece.

In the BC Supreme Court hearing where the three disgruntled trustees were contesting the land transfer, it was revealed that they had been offered double their money back but refused it, but they retaliated by charging that Asa shouldn't be allowed to hold the extra membership shares he had bought for $10,000 apiece. He was in full agreement and gave all his membership shares to his family. The judge then stipulated that amendments must be made to the constitution and bylaws governing the India Cultural Centre of Canada to make life memberships non-negotiable, non-transferable and non-refundable. When the trial was over, the three men who had gone to court to get their money from Asa went away disappointed. The judge said they had no rights and had given up their memberships on the day of the altercation. To add further insult, he ordered that the three men pay the court costs. Asa's lawyers drafted the changes the judge ordered and applied for registered charitable society status for the India Cultural Centre of Canada.

Ultimately the group decided to convert the farmhouse on Number 5 Road into a *gurdwara* and build a community centre elsewhere on the property. Both establishments became places where persons of any colour or creed or religious denomination were welcome to enter, receive food, say prayers or have a rest at any time of the day or night. Asa was made lifetime chairman, and his future efforts were aimed at encouraging development of the temple along with activities aimed at attracting the younger generations.

Most of Asa's philanthropic ventures were not as controversial as the battle to build the India Cultural Centre of Canada. Anant Pal recalls that one of the first times he saw Asa's generosity first-hand "was back in 1986 when Vancouver had Expo, and the Indian consulate in Vancouver was holding a reception for a group of children from Calcutta. They were all former prostitutes from the red light district in Calcutta, but they were talented dancers and were sponsored by this retired Indian judge who ran an organization to help street kids. So we chatted with the judge for a few minutes and left. Then Mr. Johal turned to me. 'Why don't you call this judge and let's see him in the morning for coffee.' So in the morning we went over to his hotel, and Mr. Johal gave him $100,000 without being asked. He said, 'This is for the benefit of the children.' He never told his family or consulted his wife. He just gave, no questions asked."

As Asa's businesses grew, so did the requests for gifts. Manjit explains, "The very first charity fundraiser we were asked to participate in as a family came from the International Punjabi Society." Asa's involvement with this society had begun in 1973 when he had taken his wife and daughter to India and reconnected with Shri Meharban Singh Dhupia, who had visited Vancouver in 1968. Dhupia was a regional magistrate in New Delhi, where the International Punjabi Society had begun by enlisting a handful of wealthy Sikh businessmen from around the world in order to promote the love of Punjabi culture and language. Branch offices were established in various countries to coordinate activities, and the members would meet every year for a conference. Asa, who enjoyed travelling, had been happy to join, and eventually he became president of the Vancouver branch; in this role he was often called on by the Indian consul general in Canada to entertain business owners looking for introductions or trade opportunities in the city.

Manjit describes that first fundraiser for the International Punjabi Society. "In 1987 two famous Bollywood movie stars, Sunil Dutt and Rajendra Kumar, were both in town to do some fundraising for blind people in India. Somebody called Dad from Edmonton and identified himself as the president of the International Punjabi Society, and he asked, 'Would you entertain them and do something to fundraise for them?' Dad asked Geven and me if we would help. He said, 'Financially I will support you, but I am not going to do any of the work.' Geven and I both jumped on it. She took the lead role, and I was her co-chair. We needed seven hundred people to fill the Vancouver venue, but we oversold. We had one thousand people attend that night, and it was a big success!"

Over time their meeting with the actor Sunil Dutt affected the entire Johal family because Dutt, as well as raising money for the blind, had created the Nargis Dutt

Manjit, second from the left, and Geven, fourth from the left, are
pictured here at the fundraiser they helped coordinate for the Nargis
Dutt Foundation. Asa is second from the right, and Sunil Dutt is third
from the left.

Foundation in the Punjab after the death of his wife, a clas-
sically trained Bollywood actress, in 1981 to pancreatic cancer.
When he told the family of the need for diagnostic and medical aid in the poor villages of the Punjab, Asa and Manjit
became prominent in founding a Vancouver chapter of his
foundation. Manjit then became the president and Balbir
Jawanda, an executive member of the *gurdwara* committee at
the India Cultural Centre, served as vice-president. They
raised more than $250,000 toward the purchase of a mobile
clinic to travel from village to village to provide better access

to medical care. The clinic has four examination rooms, X-ray, mammogram, blood-testing and eye-testing machines and a staff of four doctors and nurses who make ten to twelve visits to the villages annually. Ongoing fundraising by the Vancouver chapter also helps to pay the salaries of the staff. Patients diagnosed with serious ailments and those who require operations are taken to the hospital in Jalandhar with all surgeries paid for by the foundation. More recently, the Johals and their business associates in Vancouver and overseas raised another $350,000 to buy a CT scanner for the Jalandhar hospital.

"Back in the 1980s," explains Anant Pal, "the Indian community in Vancouver would hold radiothons to raise money, and Mr. Johal would always match all the funds raised. I don't have the exact number of the matched funds because virtually he did not have a limit. Some people might put a ceiling on it of $100,000 or $500,000. He never did that. In those days if you collected $250,000 or $500,000, you were quite lucky. That was a first for me. You have to remember that in the '80s there was not that kind of money in the Indian community."

Asa also became aware of the need for an auditorium at the Girls' Higher Secondary School in his father's hometown of Jandiala, a school that provided education for 750 underprivileged girls. He donated money for the construction, and then along with his friend Balbir Jawanda and his brother-in-law Sohan Basi, he helped to design it and hired the tradespeople needed to complete it. When they attended the

opening ceremonies in February 2014, the school principal
and other prominent members of the town expressed their
gratitude.

Donating money for education remained very important
to Asa, as it was the one thing he had lacked in his own life,
and he delighted in making anonymous donations to Punjabi
families in BC who could not afford to pay the university
tuition fees for their children. However, his real commitment
to higher education in this province began with a phone call
one day in February 1988 from Gurdev Attariwali, a micro-
biologist at the University of Calgary who had been attending
a conference on the West Coast. As Asa recalls it, "This lady
who I hardly knew, who grew up in the same neighbourhood as I did and was now living in Calgary, said to me on the
phone, 'Why don't you help UBC?'" Because she had known
Asa as a child, she had been given the job of contacting him
by Daniel L. Overmyer, who was at that time a professor in
the Department of Asian Studies at UBC. She explained that
some Sikhs in the BC Interior had raised $300,000 toward
funding a chair in Sikh Studies in Overmyer's department,
but it wasn't quite enough to get matching funds from the
federal Ministry of Multiculturalism because the bare min-
imum needed for the chair endowment was $700,000. Thus,
they still needed $50,000, and the government's deadline
was March 1. Asa's response to Gurdev Attariwali was, "If I
am going to do it, then I am going to do it on my own." She
recalls, "I was delighted to learn from Overmyer that within
a few days after speaking to me, Asa and Kashmir donated

$100,000 for a graduate studies scholarship fund in Punjabi language, literature and Sikh studies." And Geven comments that "it wasn't like anyone else was stepping forward to offer to do that. And it wasn't like my dad needed to do that, but he does what he thinks is necessary. He felt that it was important for the Punjabi language program, the cultural program, to be brought into the mainstream at the university level."

Asa met David Strangway, the president of UBC, a year or so after making that initial donation, by which time he had also given money to start a fund for a fellowship in forestry at the university. "Strangway had a way of getting money off of me," Asa recalls. "I gave him maybe a million or more. With David, I would just get an envelope of money and pass it to him." However, after meeting Strangway, he got more involved in the university, sitting on committees for the board of governors while continuing to support the Sikh studies program, and in 1991 he was awarded an honorary doctor of laws degree from the university in recognition of the value of his contributions as well as his achievements in the business world. And in 2007 when Strangway founded Quest University, Canada's first private, not-for-profit, secular liberal arts and sciences university in Squamish, Asa was pleased to donate $125,000 to the cause.

It was through one of Asa's grandchildren—Geven and Avtar's son Rajeev—that he became involved in philanthropy

Asa received an honorary doctor of laws degree from UBC in recognition of
his contributions to the university, as well as for his business achievements.

in the area of health and hospitals in BC. In 1984, just a year
after Rajeev was born, the little boy was diagnosed with
immune thrombocytopenic purpura (ITP), a rare blood dis-
order in which the immune system destroys the platelets
that are necessary for normal blood clotting. Bruising and
uncontrolled bleeding were just two of the symptoms.
Several doctors had diagnosed Rajeev's condition as leuk-
emia, but when the terrified parents took their son to BC
Children's Hospital, a specialist there recognized the disease
as ITP. Rajeev was given steroid injections for a year to
increase his red blood cell count and stimulate platelet count,
and over time his health stabilized.

This was an extremely difficult time for the whole Johal family, but the crisis brought the family's attention to the plight of the many other children suffering from rare diseases. When Geven became involved in the BC Children's Hospital Fashion Show and other hospital fundraising initiatives, Asa was made aware of the ongoing need for funding for more medical programs and equipment, and he began donating to the BC Children's Hospital telethon. Rajeev explains that, "*Baba Ji* and I would go to the BC Children's Miracle Network telethon to donate money. It was an annual event for us, our special outing every year. Just me and my grandfather."

Geven recalls, "That was how my dad began with the BC Children's Hospital telethon. They asked him to do some fundraising as well, but he couldn't do it because of his prior commitments, and I asked if I could do it on his behalf. My father asked, 'Do you want to?' And I said yes, as I had already co-chaired the fundraising committee for York House ... At this point, BC Children's Hospital was doing the telethon and just starting the Crystal Ball fundraising event. And so we got involved in a bigger way after that."

In 1988 the hospital's CEO, John Tegenfeldt, approached Asa to ask him to join the board of governors, and he agreed. Tegenfeldt says, "I knew Geven as she had worked with us previously, and her enthusiasm was infectious, and so we thought to ask her father. His success as a businessman appealed to us, and we thought he would be a good advisor based on his business experience. And we wanted a multicultural board of directors." Tegenfeldt was also looking for a way into the

It became an annual tradition for Asa and his grandson Rajeev to donate
money to the BC Children's Hospital.

Indo-Canadian and Chinese-Canadian communities to reflect
the diversity of BC. He knew first-hand that the ethnic communities in BC didn't have a great understanding of volunteer
involvement outside the area of religion, but this was slowly
changing over time, and the Johals helped to make those changes possible. Tegenfeldt says that even though Asa seldom
expressed his opinion during board meetings, privately he
would often provide him with valuable insight.

After Asa had been on the board of governors of BC
Children's Hospital for nearly seven years, he was recruited
by Faye Wightman, CEO of the BC Children's Hospital

Foundation, to become a member of that board. She had heard of his ability as a businessman and knew of his stature in the Indo-Canadian community, and now the foundation needed his help. "He is a very unassuming individual and comes across as being almost shy—which is an interesting juxtaposition of qualities—but he helped us by introducing the Foundation to the Indo-Canadian community as a whole. I believe he was the first Indo-Canadian to donate to BC Children's Hospital Foundation."

Besides the many projects the family helped finance at BC Children's Hospital over the years, they were also instrumental in introducing and implementing diversity protocols. In conversation with Faye Wightman one morning, Manjit suggested that it would be helpful for non-English-speaking patients to have access to interpreters, and for staff to respect Indian cultures and perhaps have the kitchen include Indian cuisine for patients, benefiting long-term stay patients by making them feel more secure. "The thing about the Johals," Wightman says, "is that they don't flaunt their wealth. As fundraisers you become aware of the families who brag about their wealth, and Asa Johal, Geven and Manjit aren't like that."

More recently the hospital made plans for a new eight-storey acute care centre. The cost would be approximately $600 million, and the Foundation's goal was to raise $200 million of that through community sponsorships. When Teri Nicholas, current CEO and president of the Foundation, told Asa of the plan, he immediately contributed the first million

Asa (centre) was recruited onto the BC Children's Hospital Foundation's board of governors by Faye Wightman (far left), the CEO of the Foundation.

dollars toward it. Faye Wightman says, "Every year for the past thirty years Asa has donated to us, and what's nice to see is that it has come full circle with the next generation of the Johal family also making contributions. Asa exemplifies values that are outstanding—the closeness of family and the desire to make the world a better place. He speaks to my heart." The Teck Acute Care Centre, which opened its doors on October 21, 2017, houses a new emergency department, radiology department, two floors of inpatient beds, an oncology unit, a pediatric intensive care unit and a neonatal intensive care unit. The hospital honours all of its million-dollar-plus sponsors with wall plaques telling their stories;

Asa and the Johal family are honoured by plaques in the ambulatory care services unit, the Royal Circle near the main entrance and in the newly built Teck Acute Care Centre.

As charity begins at home, Asa was always aware of his family's needs as well as those of the larger community. No matter how difficult the relationship was between him and his siblings, in the end he and his fortune bailed each one of them out during hard times. But he acknowledges that he always did so on the advice of his wife.

He was closest to his brother Honey, who had worked driving a truck for Terminal Sawmills for many years. Honey suffered from bouts of cancer and heart attacks throughout his life; he was seventy-five when he died in August 2005.

CHAPTER THIRTEEN

Recognition
and Awards

Asa Johal's business acumen and philanthropic activities resonated with many of his colleagues and with members of the organizations that he served over the years, and in 1991 they nominated him for two of the highest civilian honours in Canada. Although he had already received many awards, honours and other forms of acknowledgement for his achievements, these two were on another level entirely.

Early that year he was informed that he was to be awarded the Order of British Columbia, the highest form of recognition the province can extend to its citizens. It was an honour he had never expected to be given. His daughter, Geven, was thrilled to attend the ceremonies. "When they listed his accomplishments, I felt myself tearing up because he had gone from just being a hard-working person to being recognized by the whole community. He was being acknowledged not only by the Indian community, but also by the Government of BC for all the work he had done. I reminded myself of where he had come from, from being not an overly educated man to here."

A different type of man might have bragged to his friends that he was being honoured, but when given a chance to speak about it, he was too humbled to say anything. "Whatever he's got," Manjit agrees, "he's always wanted to share it and celebrate it, and that's what he did when he received the Order of BC. It was more like he was amazed. It wasn't like, 'I have accomplished this, and I am a big man.' It's not like that. My father-in-law is a person with very little ego. He is unique. He has a big presence, and his presence says things without him saying anything."

Asa was genuinely surprised when later that same year the news arrived that he had been selected to receive the Order of Canada. A Member of Parliament and friend, John Fraser, had nominated him. John Allen Fraser had been first elected to the House of Commons in 1972 from the riding of Vancouver South, which was home to a relatively large segment of the country's Indo-Canadian population. He was re-elected in 1974, 1979, 1980, 1984 and 1988 and served as minister of environment (1979–80) and minister of fisheries and oceans (1984–85) under prime ministers Joe Clark and Brian Mulroney. In 1986 he was elected Speaker of the House and served in that position until 1993, when he retired from politics.

Fraser fondly recalls his nomination of Asa Singh Johal for the Order of Canada. "I was asked by someone in the prime minister's office if I knew anyone personally from the Sikh Canadian community that the Government of Canada

Asa Johal and David Strangway, then president of the University of British Columbia, developed a close relationship that continued over the years. Strangway worked with MP John Fraser to get Asa Johal inducted into the Order of Canada.

could bestow the honour of the Order of Canada. I went to my good friend Jack Uppal—who owned Goldwood Industries on Mitchell Island, one of the oldest sawmills in BC—and asked him. Jack suggested Asa Johal, but he had introduced me to Asa much earlier in life ... and I knew of Asa's business achievements and the gifts he had given to all kinds of communities, and I could always count on him for the information I wanted or needed regarding the forest industry. He was always so knowledgeable. He was the perfect candidate for both the Order of Canada and the Order of British Columbia."

According to Asa, Fraser had always been very interested in and well connected with the Indo-Canadian community. "John Fraser is a fascinating man. When he was in Ottawa as the House Speaker, he talked me into being a director of the Canadian Development Investment Corporation in Toronto. He said, 'Asa, join! It's only six times a year so it's not that much.' So I agreed to take on the directorship. And later John Fraser and UBC President David Strangway worked behind the scenes to get me the Order of Canada."

For Asa, receiving the Order of Canada was enormously important. "It really felt good. I was the first Sikh to get the Order of Canada, and what I like about it was that I never asked anyone to get it for me. They just did it themselves. I think about it now, and it is not something I ever imagined. I always feel moved by it because of where I came from." When news of the award was published in the papers, Asa's friends from the *gurdwara* celebrated by throwing a dinner party for him at the Pan Pacific Hotel in Vancouver. Most of those who attended were prominent East Indians, but his friend, the scientist and UBC president David Strangway was also there.

Asa recalls that when he told his family, they all began making plans to attend the event, but the first order of business was to buy Asa a new suit. His wife and daughter took him downtown to be fitted by an Italian designer, and he ordered a suit in a beautiful royal blue. On October 29 the entire family ventured off on the five-and-half-hour plane ride to Ottawa. Grandson Rajeev was thrilled. "I was taken

Asa was the first Sikh to be made a member of the Order of Canada. To the left is MP John Fraser.

out of school and permitted to leave my studies to attend my grandfather's Order of Canada investiture." Besides being excited to leave school, he had the thrill of flying to Ottawa, though he was too young to really understand why they were going.

The day before the ceremony, which took place on October 31, John Fraser sent a message to Asa to say that he had arranged a private tour of the Parliament Buildings, and the whole family visited the Senate Chamber, the House of Commons and the parliamentary library with a guide who explained the inner workings of the Canadian political system. They also had an up-close look at the National Gallery of Canada and strolled around the picturesque grounds.

That evening India's high commissioner to Canada, who was immensely proud that a Canadian Sikh was finally being honoured in this way, celebrated Asa's award by throwing a lavish dinner party at his residence. He had invited a few politicians, dignitaries and entrepreneurs from Ontario as well as his family. Asa recalls, "The high commissioner of India put a dinner up for me. He asked about friends that I wanted there, and I said, 'John Fraser,' and so he came, too. I didn't know any others in the government, but there were about forty people there. I had already met the Indian high commissioner once in Vancouver, and whenever I used to go to India, he would take me to dinner all the time."

Because of the limited seating in the investiture room, the following morning the children were left behind at the hotel while Asa, Kashmir, Darcy, Manjit, Avtar and Geven made their way to the official ceremonies. Asa couldn't stop smiling that entire day. "When you're there in this room in the Parliament Buildings, you realize that many people are receiving the award. Many people who have done just as much if not more than you."

Geven recalls, "We were all just jubilant. It wasn't emotional as much as it was just exciting. Afterwards the government held a little cocktail party so you got to chat with the other twenty or so recipients and congratulate them. There was a really broad cross-section of people there from artists to businessmen, but I noticed that my dad was the only person of colour getting an award. He was receiving it for business philanthropy, but when you hear the other recipients' feats, you are in awe. I remember thinking my father is in this category with all these remarkable people! It opened my eyes to see my father differently. I hadn't seen who he was until then."

That night Asa and his family went out for a fancy meal at Hy's Encore. The entire family went this time, and Rajeev recalls that his grandfather wore his Order of Canada pin proudly. "And the grandchildren, including me, were glad that finally they could join in." Kashmir reflects on the day, "I remember he was so happy and he had a permanent smile on his face. But it didn't change him. Nothing does. He doesn't think of himself as being smarter, greater or better now. It was just a thing, and he was honoured to have it. It really felt like a gift from God."

Asa and Kashmir celebrated their seventieth wedding anniversary on December 7, 2018. Over the years since they married he has mellowed, and his relationship with Kashmir has changed. He admits to being more in love with her today than when they were young, but they have also become good friends. "We need each other more as we get older," he says. His friend Dr. Kulbir Singh feels that Asa and Kashmir "balance each other out." Asa agrees; he has also developed a firm belief in the necessity of being "in balance" and freely admits

On December 7, 2018, Asa and Kashmir celebrated seventy years of marriage.

that his life could have used more of it. As he has no hobbies aside from reading, for him life has always come down to two things: his work and his time spent with family and friends.

Although Asa Johal officially retired in 2016, his days still begin at 4:30 a.m., and he is out of the house by 5:45 to drive to the Peace Arch border crossing, arriving there precisely at 7:00 when the NEXUS lane opens. "I visit SELCO for about an hour and a half and then head back. By the time I pass White Rock, there's so much traffic you don't know if it's going to take you a half hour or fifty minutes to get home because of the Deas Island [George Massey] Tunnel." Once in Richmond, he heads to the Terminal sawmill where he inspects the entire plant.

Later in the morning Asa takes a tour of the Mainland plant, and if the weather permits he takes his dog for a walk. "My day is through at 11 o'clock, and then if I have nothing to do, I go again in the afternoon." Asa says Darcy doesn't mind him coming to check on things, and he's pleased that his son loves working with people and nurturing a good working relationship with his employees while maintaining a sense of humour.

"We are fully committed to providing durable, naturally beautiful products," Asa says when asked about the key factors involved in the company's continuing success. "Quality and customer focus are critical components of our success, and our wide range of superior products makes us a preferred supplier for many of our customers." The forest industry was, of course, more than a job for Asa. It was his calling even though, when he started, the likelihood of a person of Asian origin one day owning a sawmill here seemed absurd. But Asa had been determined to beat the odds. He has always believed his success stemmed from starting the business when he did, and that if he had started it today, the outcome would have been entirely different. "The timing," Asa says, "was crucial."

Acknowledgements

I have been very lucky to have the support of the loving people whose courage and interviews made this book possible.

First and foremost I owe a great debt to Avtar and Geven Opal for their patience and understanding. They saw the need to have Asa's story told and ran with it. My brother, Avtar, in particular, helped so much with forest industry terminology and enhanced my knowledge of the industry. I also owe gratitude to Asa and Kashmir Johal, both of whom welcomed me into their lives and allowed me to interview them in depth. I also need to thank Darcy and Manjit Johal for their candour and kindness and the Johal/Opal grandchildren, Roop, Sanjay, Rummen, Razia, Neera and Rajeev, who all participated in this project.

I would like to thank editors Peter Robson and Betty Keller at Harbour Publishing, and my husband, Michael, who had to hear this story countless times and my daughter, Schara, who has always supported my creative endeavours.

I would also like to thank the following contributors: Balbir Singh Jawanda, Sohan Singh Basi, Barry Kaye, Robert Ankner, Peter Bentley, Gerry Burch, Harry Nelson, Anant Pal Singh, Dr. Kulbir Singh, Aussie Bains, Albert Kovlaske, MP John Fraser, Harjap Dhaliwal, Richard Rajala, John Barker, Bob Sitter and Hugh Johnston.

Asa Johal's Timeline

August 17, 1922   Asa Singh Johal is born to parents Partap and Tej Kaur Johal in the village of Jandiala, Punjab, India.

1924   Asa arrives in Vancouver with his parents. Partap signs a contract with McNair Fraser Lumber Company, 8961 Shaughnessy Street, just east of the present day Oak Street Bridge off-ramp in Marpole, which at this time is part of Point Grey Municipality, not Vancouver.

1928   At age six, Asa begins attending school on Hudson Street in Marpole. All the other students are Japanese.

1929   The family moves to a rental house on Hudson Street.

1929   The family moves into a bunkhouse at McNair Fraser Lumber Company.

1930   At the age of eight, Asa transfers to David Lloyd George Elementary School at Cartier Street and 67th Avenue in Vancouver and begins grade three.

1931   Partap borrows money to buy a house on Logan Street in Marpole.

1933   Partap loses the house on Logan Street in Marpole when he can't make the payments.

1933   Asa, his parents and siblings move to a rundown shack in the lower Capilano area of North Vancouver.

1934   Partap moves his family to Alta Lake where he buys a portable sawmill. Asa attends grade six at the Alta Lake school but works for his father evenings and weekends. His mother and siblings return to Vancouver to join friends at Dominion Mills.

1934–35   Asa and Partap return to Vancouver, and Partap borrows money to buy a truck to deliver firewood as well as a house at First and Burrard, but subsequently loses both because he is unable to make the payments.

1936   The family moves to an apartment at Second Avenue and Columbia in New Westminster, and Partap finds a job on the green chain at the Canadian Western Lumber Company (Fraser Mills). Asa attends Mount Pleasant School in Vancouver.

1936   Asa, now fourteen, quits school and takes a job at Fraser Mills for twenty-five cents an hour. He lives at Fraser Mills and only comes home on weekends.

1938   Asa and his father jointly buy a house in
        Queensborough.

1940   Asa creates a company called Queensborough Fuels
        and delivers firewood and sawdust for heating all
        over Vancouver, Burnaby and New Westminster.

August 1940 Asa turns eighteen and receives his draft notice for
        the army, but a relative manages to help him avoid
        being recruited.

1941   By the end of 1941 Asa is making $1,000 a week with
        Queensborough Fuels.

1944–48 Asa holds down a part-time job at McNair Lumber
        while continuing his firewood business.

1948   At twenty-six, Asa returns to India and marries
        sixteen-year-old Kashmir Basi.

1949   Asa returns to Vancouver with Kashmir. Partap has
        taken ownership of Queensborough Fuels and the
        jointly owned house.

1949   Asa starts Pioneer Fuels and works part-time as an
        edger operator at Yukon Lumber Mill.

1950   Asa buys land on Mitchell Island and builds a small
        house for himself and Kashmir.

July 24, 1950 Asa and Kashmir's first child, Darcy, is born.

1953   Asa and Kashmir's daughter, Geven, is born.

1954   Asa's father-in-law, Hans Raj Basi, comes from India
        to live with them.

1955 Asa buys Partap's house on Mitchell Island and takes on a partner, Bruce (Jogender) Sengara, for Pioneer Fuels. Asa owns trucks and Sengara has a contract with J.R. Murray for poles. Together they build a stud mill.

1957 Asa's brother-in-law Sohan Basi comes from India to live with them.

1960 Asa ends his partnership and they divide the assets of Pioneer Fuels. Asa builds a sawmill on Mitchell Island and opens with nine employees; he sells fir, hemlock and cedar lumber to the UK.

1961 The house on Mitchell Island burns down. Asa, Kashmir and the children move into the little house while they rebuild it.

1964 Asa gets his first sales agent contract with Balfour Guthrie.

1964 Partap dies.

1967 Asa switches his sales agent to Don King of the East Asiatic Company.

1970 Darcy marries Manjit Rana.

1972 Terminal Sawmills becomes unionized.

1972 Asa attempts to buy the Anderson mill in Vancouver but is outbid by Herb Doman.

March 1973 Darcy and Manjit's first child, a daughter they name Roop, is born.

May 1973 Geven marries Avtar Opal. Asa hires him to work— at first on a part-time basis—for Terminal Sawmills.

1973   Wells Wilkinson becomes Terminal's CFO.

1973   Asa buys Burke Lumber, renames it Mainland Sawmills and converts it into a custom cutting mill.

1973   Albert Kovlaske comes to work for Terminal Sawmills.

1975   Robbie Thurston becomes Terminal's log buyer.

1975   Asa signs a cedar fibre supply and sales agreement contract with Canadian Forest Industries (Canfor). He is now exclusively cutting cedar.

1977   Asa buys an old mill in Ferndale, Washington.

1978   Asa purchases an old plywood plant on Ash Street in Marpole and renames it Mitchell Island Forest Products; it becomes his remanufacturing facility. Avtar Opal is appointed manager.

1979   Asa purchases Transco Mills, adjacent to Terminal Sawmills, renames it the Terminal Planer Mill and installs kilns to dry lumber. Asa now owns facilities for all the production stages of his lumber.

1980   Darcy becomes superintendent of Terminal Forest Products.

1982   First round of the softwood lumber dispute with the US begins.

1983-84   Japanese market for BC white wood collapses.

1984   Wildcat strike at Mainland Sawmills.

1985   Asa's mother, Tej Kaur, dies.

1985-87   The softwood lumber dispute boils over again.

1986	Asa buys the timber holdings of L&K Lumber and their 35-acre (14.2-hectare) dry land log-sorting operation in Langdale.
1991	Asa receives an honorary law degree from UBC.
1991	Asa receives both the Order of BC and the Order of Canada.
1991	Asa purchases South Everson Lumber (SELCO) in Washington state, rebuilds and modifies it to produce finished wood products.
1991	The third round of the softwood lumber dispute begins.
January 1992	Joe Johal, Asa's youngest brother, is murdered.
1993	Mitchell Island Forest Products becomes unionized.
1996	Darcy buys a mill in Lithuania.
1996	The US and Canada sign a five-year trade accord known as the Softwood Lumber Agreement (SLA), which limits annual Canadian lumber exports to the US to 14.7 billion board feet.
1997	Terminal ends its relationship with Canfor and signs a contract with Catalyst Pulp and Paper.
April 2001	The SLA expires. The US imposes 27.22 per cent duties on Canadian lumber. Fifteen thousand forest sector workers are laid off, most in BC.
2004	Mitchell Island Forest Products property is expropriated by TransLink. Asa buys 5 acres (2 hectares) next to Terminal Sawmills to build a replacement plant over the next two years.

August 2005	Asa's brother Honey dies.
2008	North America enters a recession. Asa's US sales drop by 50 per cent.
2008	Darcy's mill in Lithuania fails.
2008	Albert Kovlaske retires.
2009	TransLink disputes payment for its expropriation to Terminal. Asa sues but the lawsuit is settled out of court.
2011	Avtar Opal retires.
October 2016	Asa retires. Darcy Johal becomes president and CEO of Terminal Forest Products.

Endnotes

1   Chadney, James G. *The Sikhs of Vancouver*. New York: AMS Press, 1984. Reprinted in *Becoming Canadians: Pioneer Sikhs in Their Own Words*, by Sarjeet Singh Jagpal. Madeira Park, BC: Harbour Publishing, 1994.

2   Jagpal, Sarjeet Singh, *Becoming Canadians: Pioneer Sikhs in Their Own Words*, 34.

3   Williston, Eileen, and Betty Keller. *Forests, Power and Policy: The Legacy of Ray Williston*. Halfmoon Bay, BC: Caitlin Press, 1997. 118.

4   Fraser River Estuary Management Program. *Report of the Log Management Activity Workgroup*. March 1991. iii.

Bibliography

ARTICLES

Boyd, R., K. Doroodian, and S. Abdul-Latif. "The Effects of Tariff Removals on the North American Lumber Trade." *Canadian Journal of Agricultural Economics* 41(3): 311–28. https://onlinelibrary.wiley.com/doi/abs/10.1111/j.1744-7976.1993.tb03751.x

Dawson, M. "From 'Business as Usual' to 'Salesmanship in Reverse': Tourism Promotion in British Columbia during the Second World War." *The Canadian Historical Review* 83(2): 230–54.

Engelhardt, G.V., and J.M. Poterba. "House prices and demographic change: Canadian evidence." *Regional Science and Urban Economics* 21(4): 539–46. https://doi.org/10.1016/0166-0462(91)90017-H

Hasselback, Drew. "The granddaddy of all Canadian-US trade disputes is about to rear its ugly head again." *Financial Post*, April 24, 2017.

Huang, H., and Y. Tang. "Residential land use regulation and the US housing price cycle between 2000 and 2009." *Journal of Urban Economics* 71(1): 93–99. https://doi.org/10.1016/j.jue.2011.08.001

Kooten, G.C. van. "Economic analysis of the Canada–United States soft-wood lumber dispute: playing the quota game." *Forest Science* 48(4) : 712–21.

Mankiw, N.G., and D.N. Weil. "The Baby Boom, the Baby Bust, and the Housing Market." *Regional Science and Urban Economics* 19: 235–58. https://scholar.harvard.edu/files/mankiw/files/baby_boom.pdf

McDonnell, J.A. "World War II: Defending Park Values and Resources." *Public Historian*, 29(4): 15–33. https://doi.org/10.1525/tph.2007.29.4.15

Newton, J.L. "'These French Canadian of the Woods are Half-Wild Folk': Wilderness, Whiteness, and Work in North America, 1840–1955." *Labour/ Le Travail* 77: 121–50.

Patrias, C. "Race, Employment Discrimination, and State Complicity in Wartime Canada, 1939–1945." *Labour/ Le Travail* 59: 9–41.

Rajala, R.A. "Pulling Lumber: Indo-Canadians in the British Columbia Forest Industry, 1900–1998." *BC Historical News* 36(1): 2–13. http://www.library.ubc.ca/archives/pdfs/bchf/bchn_2002_03_winter.pdf.

Wilson, J. "Forest Conservation in British Columbia, 1935–1985: Reflections on a Barren Political Debate." *BC Studies* 76: 3–32.

BOOKS

Barman, Jean. *The West Beyond the West: A History of British Columbia*, rev. ed. Toronto: University of Toronto Press, 1996.

Belshaw, John Douglas, and David J. Mitchell. "The Economy Since the Great War." *The Pacific Province: A History of British Columbia*. Hugh Johnston, ed. Vancouver: Douglas & McIntyre, 1996.

Buchignani, Norman, Doreen M. Indra and Ram Srivastiva. *Continuous Journey: A Social History of South Asians in Canada*. Toronto: McClelland & Stewart, 1985.

Chadney, James G. *The Sikhs of Vancouver*. New York: AMS Press, 1984. Reprinted in *Becoming Canadians: Pioneer Sikhs in Their Own Words* by Sarjeet Singh Jagpal. Madeira Park, BC: Harbour Publishing, 1994.

Gregson, Harry. *A History of Victoria, 1842–1970*. Victoria, BC: Victoria Observer Publishing, 1970.

Jagpal, Sarjeet Singh. *Becoming Canadians: Pioneer Sikhs in Their Own Words*. Madeira Park, BC: Harbour Publishing, 1994.

Jensen, Joan M. *Passage from India: Asian Indian Immigrants in North America*. New Haven, CT: Yale University Press, 1988.

Johnston, Hugh M. *The Voyage of the Komagata Maru: The Sikh Challenge to Canada's Colour Bar*, 2nd edition. Vancouver: UBC Press, 1989.

MacDonald, Norbert. *Distant Neighbors: A Comparative History of Seattle and Vancouver*. Lincoln, NE: University of Nebraska Press, 1987.

Mahood, Ian, and Ken Drushka. *Three Men and a Forester*. Madeira Park, BC: Harbour Publishing, 1990.

Marchak, Patricia. *Green Gold: The Forest Industry in British Columbia*. Vancouver: UBC Press, 1983.

Morley, Alan. *Vancouver: From Milltown to Metropolis*, 2nd ed. Vancouver: Mitchell Press, 1969.

Ormsby, Margaret A. *British Columbia: A History*. Vancouver: Macmillan, 1958.

References

TELEPHONE INTERVIEWS

Ankner, Robert (November 10, 2017)

Attariwali, Gurdev, (September 23, 2017)

Bains, Aussie. (December 12, 2016)

Bentley, Peter (November 12, 2017)

Bogel, Tim, Ph.D., Manager, Research, Economic Services Branch ,
    Ministry of Forest, Lands, and Natural Resources, Government of
    BC, Economist (April 2018 by phone and email)

Burch, Gerry (October 30, 2017)

Dhaliwal, Harjap (November 28, 2017)

Johal, Asa (November 6, 2017)

Johal, Kashmir (October 22, 27, 2017)

Opal, Avtar (December 6, 8, 11, 12, 2017; February 12, 18, March 6, 9,
    June 10, 2018)

Opal, Geven (December 8, 10, 12, 2017)

Singh, Dr. Kulbir (October 23, 2017)

Zhang, Theresa, Senior Manager, Trade and Export Policy Branch,
    Ministry of Forests, Lands, and Natural Resources and Rural
    Development, Government of BC

PERSONAL INTERVIEWS

Basi, Sohan (March 15, 2017)

Basran, Roop (March 27, 2017)

Fraser, John, MP (November 12, 2016)

Jawanda, Balbir (November 23, 25, 2016)

Johal, Asa (December 5, 12, 15, 2016; February 18, April 12,
    November 3, 7, 2017)

Johal, Darcy (September 18, November 5, 2017)

Johal, Kashmir (December 11, 2016; November 23, October 12, 2017)

Johal, Manjit (November 22, 2016; February 11, 2017)

Kovlaske, Albert (December 8, 2016)

Nelson, Harry (November 2, 2017)

Opal, Avtar (November 4, 2016; February 9, October 3, 2017)

Opal, Geven (November 3, 2016; March 17, 2017)

Opal, Neera (October 5, 2016)

Opal, Rajeev (October 6, 2017)

Opal, Razia (February 12, 2017)

Singh, Anant Pal (November 17, 2016)

Index

Page numbers in **bold** refer to photographs.